# PRACTICAL OSCILLATOR

# Other Titles of Interest

# PRACTICAL OSCILLATOR
# CIRCUITS

by

## A. FLIND

**BERNARD BABANI (publishing) LTD**
**THE GRAMPIANS**
**SHEPHERDS BUSH ROAD**
**LONDON W6 7NF**
**ENGLAND**

# Please Note

Although every care has been taken with the production of this book to ensure that any projects, designs, modifications and/or programs, etc., contained herewith, operate in a correct and safe manner and also that any components specified are normally available in Great Britain, the Publishers do not accept responsibility in any way for the failure, including fault in design, of any project, design, modification or program to work correctly or to cause damage to any other equipment that it may be connected to or used in conjunction with, or in respect of any other damage or injury that may be so caused, nor do the Publishers accept responsibility in any way for the failure to obtain specified components.

Notice is also given that if equipment that is still under warranty is modified in any way or used or connected with home-built equipment then that warranty may be void.

© 1996 BERNARD BABANI (publishing) LTD

First Published – May 1996

**British Library Cataloguing in Publication Data**

A catalogue record for this book is available from the British Library

ISBN 0 85934 393 6

Cover Design by Gregor Arthur
Printed and bound in Great Britain by Cox & Wyman Ltd, Reading

# Preface

Oscillators are the prime movers in practically all electronic circuits. Often an oscillator will be part of the circuit itself, generating a signal which is processed elsewhere to create the desired output. In other cases it might be remote, such as a distant radio transmitter, but even here most receivers incorporate oscillators of their own for use in signal processing. Indeed, it could be said that the oscillator is one of the most vital and frequently used types of circuit around.

To suit the huge variety of applications for oscillators there are many types of circuit for them. The aim of this book is to present a wide range of these for enthusiasts to construct, experiment with and perhaps use in their own designs. The accent where possible is on the promotion of a thorough understanding of their operation. Basic circuits are covered, but where possible unusual techniques are also shown to encourage experimenters to develop novel designs of their own. All the circuits offered have been carefully "bench tested" to ensure that they will work correctly, and the advantages and limitations of each are explained clearly to enable the best choice to be made.

The oscillators are grouped into three main categories. The first covers circuits using resistors and capacitors to determine the output frequency, and these are further divided into four groups according to the type of active device used with them. The first covers the ICM7555 and ICM7556 timer ICs. These versatile devices are ideal for oscillator design, used either by themselves or together with other devices such as op-amps. The next section covers designs employing various CMOS ICs, built from both individual gates and with special purpose-designed ICs. This section ends with a circuit for the reliable generation of "white" and "pink" noise which has various uses, especially in sound effect creation, but is often difficult to produce. Op-amps can be used as oscillators so this is covered too, including a circuit for a practical high-quality audio signal generator. Finally the 8030 and the newer MAX038 "waveform generator" ICs are described, with details of their basic circuit configurations.

The next group covers circuits using inductance and capacitance for setting the output frequency. These are not so easy to adjust as the resistor and capacitor types but are much more stable, especially at higher frequencies. It is not always appreciated that they can be used at relatively low frequencies, or that some of the circuits using them can be very simple indeed. For example, very stable signal sources may easily be built with small, inexpensive chokes and single CMOS gates, and if necessary a CMOS divider can reduce the frequency. Transistor and FET L-C circuits are also covered in detail.

Circuits using crystals to determine the output frequency are described next. These are extremely stable, and the increasing availability of both crystals and special ICs for driving them are making crystal oscillator design much easier than it once was. Sometimes a single IC containing a built-in crystal and a programmable output divider can be used to generate an accurate reference frequency.

The final chapter describes practical construction techniques using "stripboard", using one of the circuits shown earlier as an example. This can be used to make a useful piece of audio test equipment which should find a place in many readers' workshops.

There is much pleasure and interest to be obtained from experiments with oscillator design. Hopefully this book will encourage readers to venture into this area of the hobby for themselves by building and modifying the circuits shown, and then perhaps producing new designs of their own.

*A. Flind*

# Contents

# Chapter 1

## TIMER BASED OSCILLATORS

**The ICM7555 and ICM7556 Timers**

One of the easiest ways to create an oscillator circuit is with an ICM7555 timer IC. This chip is so useful for oscillator design that it is worth taking a little time to understand its internal structure and operation in detail. A thorough grasp of this will allow the enthusiast to create endless ingenious oscillator circuits using a minimum of additional external parts.

The prefix "7" indicates that this is the CMOS "micropower" version of the device, which offers some significant advantages over its older bipolar stablemate. To begin with it draws much less current from the power supply and can operate from lower voltages. Supplies from as low as three volts up to a maximum of fifteen volts can be used with a typical drain of around a hundred microamps, making this the ideal choice for battery-powered circuits. When lightly loaded the output voltage swings practically all the way to both supply rails, a feature which can greatly improve frequency stability in many oscillator designs. Input impedances are much higher than those of the bipolar version, allowing the use of small capacitors together with high resistance values in low-frequency circuits. Finally, it doesn't need the local "decoupling" capacitors for the supply and "control" connections required by the bipolar type, although as always there should be some decoupling included in the circuit. One word of warning; being CMOS, the ICM7555 is rather prone to damage by static, so experimenters are advised to take suitable precautions such as the use of an earthed wrist strap when handling this chip.

A simplified version of the ICM7555 internal construction is shown in Figure 1.1. It has two inputs, "trigger" and "threshold", which go to a pair of internal comparators. The other two comparator inputs are provided with reference voltages of one third and two-thirds of the supply voltage from an internal chain of three identical resistors, and their outputs go to the "set" and "reset" inputs of a flip-flop which drives the output. The flip-flop also drives a "discharge" transistor with an open

1

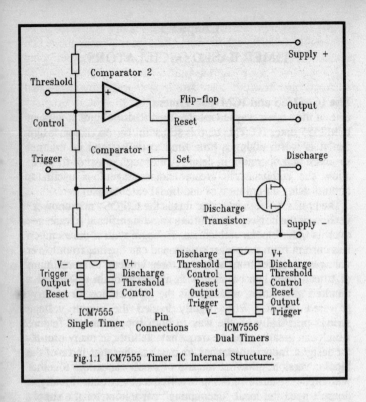

Fig.1.1 ICM7555 Timer IC Internal Structure.

collector, intended for discharging the capacitor used in timing circuits. In these CMOS versions of the device this is, of course, the drain of an FET. The "control" input is a direct connection to the upper reference voltage and can be used to force this higher or lower. This affects both reference voltages of course, but it alters the higher one by twice as much as the lower so it can be used for frequency adjustment. There is also a "reset" input, not shown in Fig.1.1, which forces the flip-flop into the "reset" state if taken low. In most oscillator circuits this is not needed so it is disabled by direct connection to the positive supply.

The IC operates as follows. If the voltage at the "trigger" input falls below a third of the supply voltage, the output of comparator 1 goes high, "setting" the flip-flop. This causes the output to go high (positive) and the discharge transistor to be turned off. If the "threshold" input voltage now rises above two thirds of the supply the flip-flop is reset, with the output going low (negative) and the discharge resistor being turned on. In oscillator applications, the two inputs are often connected together and used as a single input so that the circuit becomes a "Schmitt" device with accurate thresholds. It should be noted that this "inverts" the input voltage, with the output going high for an input below the lower reference and low as it rises above the upper one.

The ICM7555 is available in the common 8-pin DIL package and there is also a dual version, the ICM7556, with two timers contained in a single14-pin DIL package. Pin connections for both are shown in the drawing. They can operate at frequencies up to about 500kHz and with their high input impedance and reasonable output drive capability it can be seen that these cheap and readily available ICs can be used in an unlimited variety of oscillator designs. In the next few pages some of these will be described.

### The Basic ICM7555 Oscillator Circuit

Figure 1.2. shows the standard "astable" oscillator circuit for the ICM7555 timer. This is the basic circuit that is shown in most component catalogues and other sources of 555 IC information. In operation, capacitor C1 is charged and discharged repeatedly between the internal reference voltages of one third and two-thirds of the supply voltage. During the charging part of the cycle current flows into the capacitor from the positive supply through R1 and R2. The output, from pin 3, is high (positive) and the discharge transistor's drain, pin 7, is "off". This state continues until the voltage across C1 reaches two-thirds of the supply, when the internal flip-flop changes state, the output goes low (negative) and the discharge transistor is turned on. The drain of this transistor now pulls pin 7 down almost to the negative supply potential. The current from R1 is now diverted into pin 7 and C1 begins discharging into it through R2. Discharge continues until the voltage across C1 has fallen to one third of the supply voltage when the flip-flop state is again changed, turning off the discharge transistor and driving the output high, and the whole cycle repeats.

3

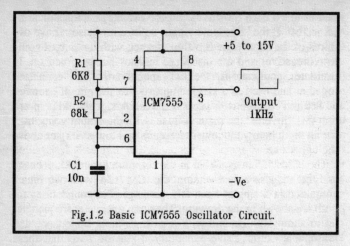

Fig.1.2 Basic ICM7555 Oscillator Circuit.

The charging and discharging of the capacitor is exponential in nature, but for a change of one third of the supply voltage with an effective starting voltage of two-thirds of the supply, the time, or period, of each half cycle is very nearly $0.7 \times R \times C$. Of course, "R" for charging is R1+R2 whilst "R" for discharging is just R2, so the total period per cycle can be calculated from:

$$t = 0.7 \times (R1+(2 \times R2)) \times C1 \text{ seconds.}$$

and the frequency, which is always 1/t, is therefore :

$$f = \frac{1}{0.7 \times (R1+(2 \text{ x } R2)) \times C1} \text{ Hz.}$$

The values in these formula are, like all those given in this book, expressed in ohms, farads, seconds and hertz so the necessary compensation should be made in calculations to allow for this. With the values shown in Figure 1.2 the output will be about 1kHz but frequencies can be from many seconds per cycle up to 500kHz and perhaps more. At high frequencies the effects of stray capacitance and internal propagation delays usually result in a lower frequency than calculations might suggest so a little practical testing is advisable. The capacitor

4

value can be from a few tens of picofarads to many microfarads and, as the device has the very high input impedance typical of CMOS, resistors can have values from around 4k7 up to 10 megohms or more. Although ICM7555 oscillator circuits are sometimes seen using electrolytic capacitors for "C" this is not really recommended. The wide manufacturing tolerance allowed in electrolytic capacitance values together with their unpredictable leakage currents makes them generally unsuitable for timing or frequency control. Where a low frequency is required it's better by far to use a CMOS divider, a technique which will be covered later in this book. Ceramic capacitors are also best avoided where stability is important because their values often change significantly with temperature. Polyester, polystyrene and silver-mica types are best.

An advantage of this circuit is that the output is not part of the frequency generating network so loads connected to it have no effect on the frequency. With the old bipolar type of 555 small loudspeakers were often driven directly by the output. Whilst the CMOS version doesn't have the power for this it can drive piezo transducers very effectively, and a simple buffer circuit could be used for higher power. Because the switching points and the charge-discharge rates are proportional to the supply voltage, variations of supply voltage have virtually no effect on frequency.

There are some disadvantages with this circuit. It cannot generate a true "squarewave" output. Because of the different values of resistance present in the charge and discharge portions of the cycle the charging time will always be longer than the discharge time, so the output can never be symmetrical. If something approaching a squarewave is required R1 will have to be small in comparison with R2, which raises the current through R1 during the discharge cycle, increasing the overall consumption and the saturation voltage across the discharge transistor. This may adversely affect frequency calculations, already complex because of the two resistance values. There is another arrangement, which for many applications may be better, as will be seen in the next circuit.

*Components for Figure 1.2*

*Resistors* (metal film, 0.6W)
R1              6k8
R2              68k

*Capacitor*
C1              10nF polyester

*Semiconductor*
IC1             CM7555 CMOS timer.

## Alternative ICM7555 Oscillator Circuit

A glance at the circuit of Figure1.3 will show how much simpler this is compared to the previous arrangement. Just one resistor and one capacitor are used with the ICM7555 to create a stable and reliable oscillator with an output that is a true squarewave. The operation is simpler to follow, too. Whilst the output of the IC is positive it charges the capacitor C1 through resistor R1. When the voltage across C1 reaches two-thirds of the supply the IC output changes state, going low and discharging C1 through R1. When the capacitor voltage has dropped to a third of the supply, the IC output again changes state and the cycle repeats.

The calculations are easier too. Each half cycle is still calculated from $0.7 \times R \times C$, but there is now only one value of R to consider, so the total period is given by:

$$t = 1.4 \times R \times C$$

and the frequency, the inverse of this, is given by:

$$f = \frac{1}{(1.4 \times R \times C)}.$$

This is much simpler than the formula for the previous circuit. The component values shown result in a frequency of about 1050Hz, but like the previous circuit this arrangement can operate at frequencies up to around 500kHz.

This circuit doesn't work so well with the bipolar type of 555

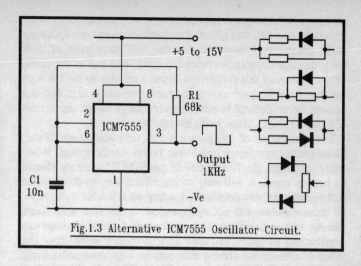

Fig.1.3 Alternative ICM7555 Oscillator Circuit.

IC but with the CMOS ICM7555 version performance is excellent. The output has a near-perfect 50-50 duty cycle, the frequency is substantially stable right across the supply voltage range and the current consumption is smaller, making this a better choice for battery operation. Frequency trimming is simple too. A variable resistor can be used in series with the fixed one to give the required range of adjustment. If a non-symmetrical output is needed this can be obtained by using one or more diodes to alter the effective resistor values for charging and discharging the capacitor. Any of the networks shown to the right of the circuit can be used in place of resistor R1 to achieve this. The top two examples both produce shorter positive output half-cycles, reversing the diode would shorten the negative ones. The third network gives independent control of each half-cycle, whilst the last provides duty cycle variation that is practically independent of operating frequency. A practical application for this might be in simple power control, such as a cavers' lamp with variable brilliance to conserve battery power.

This is a good point to pause and explain a disadvantage of frequency adjustment with a variable resistor in this type of circuit. It is actually the oscillator period that is directly proportional to the resistance value, not the frequency. The frequency, as shown in the above formulae, is inversely proportional to the period. In practice this means that frequency controls spanning ratios greater than about five to one will have most of their control range hopelessly compressed into one end of the scale. One way around this problem is to use a multi-way switch with suitable fixed resistor values for each frequency step, but if a smooth linear control is needed over a large range, the circuit of Figure 1.7 will show how this can be achieved.

The advantages of this circuit are its simplicity, ease of use, better output symmetry and lower power consumption. When using it though, the limitations of the ICM7555 output should be kept in mind. It will only swing all the way to the positive and negative supply rails if the loading on it is kept light. Also, its drive capability is not symmetrical, it can sink a lot more current to negative than it can source as a positive output so overloading is likely to cause loss of output symmetry. The value of resistor R1 should therefore be kept reasonably high, not less than 10k. To obtain an output without loading it there are several options. The circuit being driven may have a high enough impedance input in any case. CMOS gates can be driven without problems, in fact one could be used as a buffer. The "discharge" connection at pin 7 is not used by this circuit, which creates some interesting possibilities. To avoid output loading the signal can be taken from this instead, using a "pull-up" resistor to the positive supply. This could provide a TTL-compatible output with the pull-up resistor connected to the TTL's 5-volt positive supply. A variable DC voltage might be applied to the pull-up resistor, resulting in an output with the frequency of the oscillator but having an amplitude directly proportional to the applied voltage. This could doubtless find some really interesting applications. Finally, an ICM7556 dual timer might be used, with the inputs of the second timer connected to the output of the first to create a buffer.

*Components for Figure 1.3*

*Resistor*
R1                    68k metal film, 0.6W

*Capacitor*
C1                10nF polyester

*Semiconductors*
Diodes            Any small silicon signal type, 1N4148 etc.
IC1               ICM7555 CMOS timer.

## Voltage Controlled Oscillator

Now that the basic ICM7555 oscillator circuits have been covered, some more interesting circuits can be described. Voltage controlled oscillators are frequently needed by circuit designers, and are often designed around 555 timer ICs. The method generally used is to charge the timing capacitor with a voltage-controlled constant current, often from a transistor, and discharge it with the internal transistor in the timer. The output from this type of circuit is a stream of pulses of constant width, with the time between them being voltage controlled. This arrangement has a couple of disadvantages. The charging current must come from the positive supply so the control voltage must be relative to this and become increasingly negative for an increase in frequency. Control signals are usually relative to negative supply however, and positive-going, so a "current mirror" circuit is needed. The other problem is that the output pulses from this version of the circuit are negative, but many designs work better with positive pulses. A circuit having neither of these drawbacks is shown in Figure 1.4.

This circuit is the reverse of the version described above. The discharge of capacitor C1 is voltage controlled, with short charging pulses controlled by the discharge transistor of IC2. To follow the operation, assume that the output from pin 3 of timer IC2 is low and the discharge transistor pin 7 is on, drawing current through R6 to turn on transistor TR3. This transistor holds the base of TR2 at the positive supply potential, ensuring that it is off. The capacitor C1 can therefore discharge through R4 at a rate determined by the collector current of TR1. As the voltage across it falls to a third of the supply voltage, the timer output goes high. At the same time the discharge transistor and TR3 turn off, so current from R3 now turns on TR2, which charges C1 through R4. When the voltage across C1 reaches two-thirds of the supply voltage, IC2 again changes

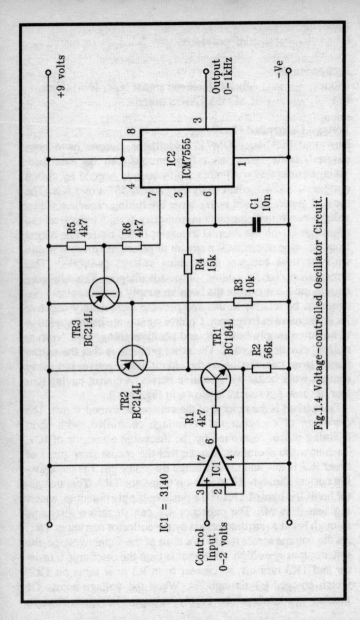

Fig.1.4 Voltage–controlled Oscillator Circuit.

10

state and the cycle recommences.

A characteristic of transistors is that nearly all the current flowing into the emitter flows out again from the collector. A minute part flows out through the base, but this is usually so small it can be ignored. Since the emitter voltage follows the voltage applied to the base, less the "base-emitter drop" of about 0.6 volts, this can be used to control the voltage across the emitter resistor, R2 in this circuit. The base voltage therefore controls the current from the collector, creating a voltage-controlled current source. The control voltage can be applied directly to the base of TR1 to control the frequency in this circuit, but if an op-amp is used with the transistor as shown the voltage across R2 will correspond almost exactly to the input voltage, with the op-amp automatically compensating for the emitter-base voltage drop and variations of this with temperature. The resulting output frequency control range will then start from zero instead of 0.6 volts.

Design calculations for this circuit are a little more complex than those for the simple fixed-frequency circuits and a few design rules have to be observed. R4 should be fairly low in comparison with R2. There must always be enough voltage across TR1 for it to operate, so the input should never exceed a value of about a volt below a third of the supply. This circuit is sensitive to supply voltage changes, so the supply may have to be regulated. Once it has been decided what the maximum control voltage is going to be, the period for the discharge part of each cycle can be calculated from:

$$t = \frac{C \times R \times E}{V}$$

Where C is the value of the timing capacitor C1, R is the value of emitter resistor R2, E is a third of the supply voltage and V is the voltage across R2. To this should be added the time for the charging part of the cycle:

$$t = 0.7 \times C1 \times R4$$

These two together give the total period per cycle so, as always, their inverse gives the corresponding frequency. With the component values shown and a supply of 9 volts the circuit generates a frequency output from zero to about 1kHz for an input of 0 to 2 volts. The output consists of positive pulses of about 100μs width, ideal for making lots of noise with a small loudspeaker with the simplest of output buffers, perhaps a single transistor. With a 1n capacitor for C1 it produces just over 9 kHz for the same input voltage range, with correspondingly shorter output pulses. Note that if an op-amp is used as shown it must be of a type with inputs and output capable of operating down to the negative supply potential. The CA3140 shown is suitable, other possibles are the CA3130, or one of the amps in a CA3240, an LM358 or an LM324. Other transistors can be used in place of the types shown, so long as they are of correct polarity.

The usefulness of this circuit is limited mainly to audio work, but is cheap, simple and fairly stable.

*Components for Figure 1.4*

*Resistors* (all metal film, 0.6W)

| | |
|---|---|
| R1 | 4k7 |
| R2 | 56k |
| R3 | 10k |
| R4 | 15k |
| R5 | 4k7 |
| R6 | 4k7 |

*Capacitor*

| | |
|---|---|
| C1 | 10n polyester |

*Semiconductors*

| | |
|---|---|
| IC1 | CA3140 op-amp |
| IC2 | ICM7555 CMOS timer |
| TR1 | BC184L |
| TR2 | BC214L |
| TR3 | BC214L |

# Voltage Controlled Oscillator Using ICM7556

In the last circuit, transistors were used for generating a constant current and for inverting the discharge output from a timer IC in the design of a voltage controlled oscillator circuit. To demonstrate the possibilities, here's a completely different approach to VCO design with an op-amp integrator replacing the timing capacitor and current source and an ICM7556 dual timer providing the inversion.

An op-amp integrator has two inputs, a non-inverting one which is usually connected to a reference voltage, and an inverting one to which an input voltage is connected through a resistor with negative feedback from the output applied through a capacitor. Within the constraints of supply voltage, the op-amp uses the feedback to keep the voltage at the inverting input equal to that at the non-inverting one. This means that if a steady voltage is applied to the input resistor the potential across it will be the difference between this and the reference voltage so a constant current flows into the input as a result. The feedback capacitor is charged by this current, so to keep the inverting input voltage constant the op-amp output voltage changes at a constant rate. This can be used to design an oscillator, switching the input voltage polarity as the output passes the input thresholds of a timer IC. One minor difficulty is that the integrator output is inverted, falling for a positive input and rising with negative. To make a workable oscillator with the inverting ICM7555 there must be a polarity reversal at some point. One way to do this is with a dual op-amp, with the second inverting the output of the first. This requires at least two more resistors however, and can limit the frequency of the circuit. A better approach is to use a dual timer, with the second acting as an inverter for the output of the first.

Figure 1.5 shows a circuit that operates in this way. IC1 is the integrator, with a reference of about a third of the supply voltage applied to its non-inverting input, pin 3, by resistors R3 and R4. Whilst the discharge transistor of the second timer, pin 13, is off, a voltage greater than the reference applied to resistor R1 will cause the output of IC1 to decrease at a rate determined by the input voltage and the values of R1, R2 and capacitor C1. When it reaches a third of the supply voltage, the first timer changes state with its output, pin 5, going high. This is

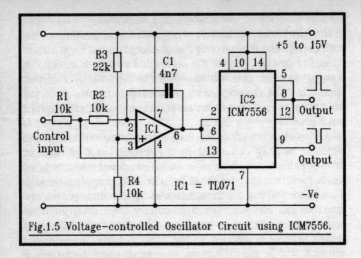

Fig.1.5 Voltage–controlled Oscillator Circuit using ICM7556.

connected to the inputs of the second timer, pins 8 and 12, so the output of this now goes low and its discharge transistor, pin 13, turns on. The integrator now has an effective negative input of about a third of the supply connected to R2, so its output starts to rise. When it reaches two thirds of the supply voltage the two timers change state again and the cycle repeats.

The time for the first part of the cycle is given by:

$$t = \frac{C \times R \times V}{E}$$

Where C is C1, R is R1 + R2, V is a third of the supply voltage and E is the applied input voltage.

The time for the second part of the cycle can be determined by a similar formula, but in this case R is R2 alone and V and E are approximately equal in value, so the time is given simply by:

$$t = C1 \times R2.$$

As with the previous circuit, these two can be added together to obtain the total period for each complete cycle, and the

14

inverse of this gives the frequency. The values shown produce 50μs pulses with a frequency of 10kHz for an input equal to the supply voltage.

This is an easier circuit for experimenters to work with than the previous one. The input voltage may be equal to or even higher than the positive supply. Higher frequencies can be reliably achieved, so long as a suitably short output pulse width is set with R2 and C1. The fact that the control voltage must be higher than a third of the reference might be a disadvantage but this can be offset elsewhere, perhaps by a resistor between the input and the positive rail. The output point shown, from pin 5, consists of positive pulses but negative ones are also available from pin 9 and the discharge transistor of the first timer, which is off during output pulses, is also available at pin 1. The op-amp does not have to be a type able to operate with inputs and output at negative supply potential like that of the previous circuit, the TL071 shown was found to work particularly well in this arrangement. The main disadvantage is perhaps the extra cost of the dual timer, but the circuit uses fewer components and is simpler to construct than the transistor version.

*Components for Figure 1.5*

*Resistors* (all metal film, 0.6W )

| | |
|---|---|
| R1 | 10k |
| R2 | 10k |
| R3 | 22k |
| R4 | 10k |

*Capacitor*

| | |
|---|---|
| C1 | 4n7 polyester |

*Semiconductors*

| | |
|---|---|
| IC1 | TL071 op-amp, FET input. |
| IC2 | ICM7556 dual CMOS timer |

**Simple Triangle Wave Generator**

Now that the use of an integrator and dual timer as an oscillator has been described, it is worth looking at a few more circuit configurations using these A very simple circuit can be

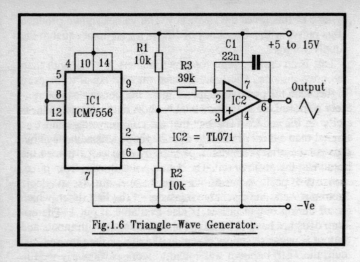

Fig.1.6 Triangle-Wave Generator.

constructed with a dual timer and an op-amp integrator to produce a signal with a triangular waveform. The circuit for this is shown in Figure 1.6. This again uses the ICM7556 dual timer IC to make a "non-inverting" timer for use with an inverting integrator. The difference is that here the input to the integrator is taken from the timer output and its reference voltage is set by R1 and R2 to half the supply voltage. Equal and opposite input voltages are therefore applied to the integrator input depending on the timer output state, so its output increases and decreases at the same rate in both directions. Note that this would not be the case with the older bipolar type of 556 timer, where the output does not switch all the way to both supply voltages like that of the CMOS micropower version. As the timer output changes state as the integrator output reaches one third and two thirds of the supply voltage, the triangle wave always has a peak-to-peak amplitude of one third of the supply.

The frequency of this circuit is determined entirely by the values of R3 and C1 and is virtually independent of the supply voltage. The period for half a cycle is given by $0.667 \times R \times C$, so the overall period is twice this:

$$t = 1.333 \times R \times C$$

16

giving a frequency of :

$$f = \frac{1}{1.333 \times R \times C}$$

As always, stray capacitance and propagation delays can cause performance to differ a little from calculated values especially at higher frequencies, so practical testing should be carried out before finalising circuit design. With the values shown the circuit produces an output of about 1kHz, but it has been tested with the op-amp shown at frequencies well in excess of 100kHz and there was very little visible distortion of the triangular waveform. The output, as it is taken from the output of the op-amp, has a relatively low impedance. Loads as low as 100 ohms can be driven easily.

In addition to the triangular waveform, squarewave outputs are available from pins 5 and 9 of IC1 although these should not be loaded too much. The two discharge outputs from pins 1 and 13 are also available if required.

This circuit shows just how simple it can be to construct a reliable oscillator with an ICM7556 and very few external parts. In the next circuit a version with linear frequency control will be shown.

*Components for Figure 1.6*

*Resistors* (all metal film, 0.6W)
R1          10k
R2          10k
R3          39k

*Capacitors*
C1          22nF, polystyrene or polyester.

*Semiconductors*
IC1          ICM7556 dual timer, CMOS version.
IC2          TL071 JFET input op-amp.

**Variable Frequency Triangle Wave Generator
with Linear Control**

During the description of Figure 1.2, it was explained that the "period" of a simple 555 oscillator circuit was linearly related to the resistor and that if this was made variable with the object of providing frequency adjustment, the scale of the resulting control would have most of its range compressed into one end. For applications requiring a linear frequency control the circuit of Figure 1.7 can be used instead.

The operation of this circuit is similar to that of Figure 1.6, using an ICM7556 dual timer connected as a "non-inverting" timer for use with an inverting integrator configured from IC2b. However, instead of being connected directly to the output of the timer as before, the input to the integrator, to resistor R4, is first attenuated by the variable resistor VR1. This controls the proportion of the timer output voltage applied, which alters the rate at which the output voltage of the integrator increases and decreases, and this has the effect of altering the output frequency. A little mathematical formula-tweaking can be used to show that the frequency is directly proportional to the integrator input voltage so in turn it is almost directly proportional to the position of the control VR1, there being only a slight error due to loading of VR1 by R4. A low-impedance point at half the supply voltage is required for the low end of the variable resistor and this is provided by the voltage dividing resistors R1 and R2 and a unity-gain buffer made from IC2a, the second op-amp in the package. The two op-amps are contained in a TL072, which is a dual version of the TL071 supplied in a single 8-pin DIL package.

Period and frequency calculations for the maximum frequency of this circuit are similar to those of the circuit of Figure 1.6. R3 sets the minimum frequency, in this case a tenth of the maximum. If R3 is omitted, the frequency control range will extend right down to zero. The maximum frequency, with VR1 the wiper of VR1 at the IC1 output end, can be calculated from:

$$f = \frac{1}{1.333 \times R4 \times C3}$$

With the values shown the range is approximately 1kHz to

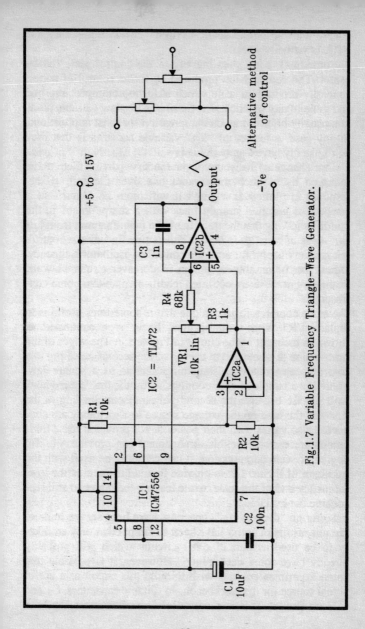

Fig.1.7 Variable Frequency Triangle-Wave Generator.

Alternative method
of control

10kHz and the output scale, using a "linear" component for VR1, is virtually linear.

Sometimes, some non-linearity of the control scale can be useful. The compression produced by linear control of period generally produces a scale which is far too cramped into one end to be of any practical use. Similarly, log-law variable resistors usually offer too much compression for most applications. In any case, a feature of "log" variable resistors is that they don't usually have a smooth log law at all! Mostly they provide a slow change of resistance over the first part of their range followed by a much more rapid one over the rest. If this response is plotted as a graph it will often be found that it consists of just two straight lines with a sharp "knee" in the middle, showing that the track has been manufactured from just two types of resistive material. This is fine for volume control, but not very useful for accurate control of oscillator frequency. Other types of variable resistor are made, inverse square law for example, but these are not often readily available to home constructors.

A scale compression technique that is sometimes useful is to replace VR1 with a dual-ganged linear type connected as shown to the right of the circuit in Figure 1.7. The wiper of the first section is connected to the top of the second, resulting in a control scale following something similar to a square law. There are a couple of shortcomings with this; the "square law" isn't precise because the second pot represents loading to the first and the load on the voltage source to which they are connected also varies with their position, but provided these limitations are catered for this arrangement can provide a useful degree of scale compression. It can certainly be used with the oscillator of Figure 1.7. to provide finer adjustment at the low-frequency end of the scale, while leaving the high end still reasonable controllable.

So far no "decoupling" capacitors have been shown in these circuits, as the majority have been so simple that they are likely to be used as part of other circuits which will probably already have some decoupling . However, it is possible that some experimenters may wish to build this circuit as a useful signal source for the workbench, so suitable capacitors, C1 and C2, are shown. This is a very useful oscillator that has been employed by the author in a number of designs needing a reliable and easily controlled frequency source. It can operate from sub-audio to moderately high frequencies, well above 100kHz if required. The outputs available are the triangle wave from IC2b, squarewaves from IC1 pins 5 and 9, and as with the previous circuit the discharge transistor collectors are both available at IC1 pins 1 and 13.

*Components for Figure 1.7*

*Resistors* (all metal film, 0.6W)
| | |
|---|---|
| R1 | 10k |
| R2 | 10k |
| R3 | 1k |
| R4 | 68k |
| VR1 | 10k linear pot, carbon |

*Capacitors*
| | |
|---|---|
| C1 | 10µF/25V electrolytic |
| C2 | 100nF ceramic |
| C3 | 1nF polyester or polystyrene |

*Semiconductors*
| | |
|---|---|
| IC1 | ICM7556 dual timer, CMOS |
| IC2 | TL072 dual JFET input op-amp. |

## Spot Frequency Function Generator

Figure 1.6 showed a circuit using an integrator with an ICM7556. The effect of the integrator, when supplied with a squarewave input from the timer, was to convert it into a triangle wave. If the triangle-wave signal is applied to another integrator it will be modified further, this time into a sinewave. This process can be used to generate a fairly pure sinewave of fixed frequency with a relatively simple circuit. The version shown here generates all three basic waveforms, square, triangle and sine, at approximately equal peak-to-peak voltage amplitudes. With a nine-volt supply the amplitude of the sinewave, three volts peak-to-peak, is roughly equivalent to 1 volt RMS, a useful value for audio testing.

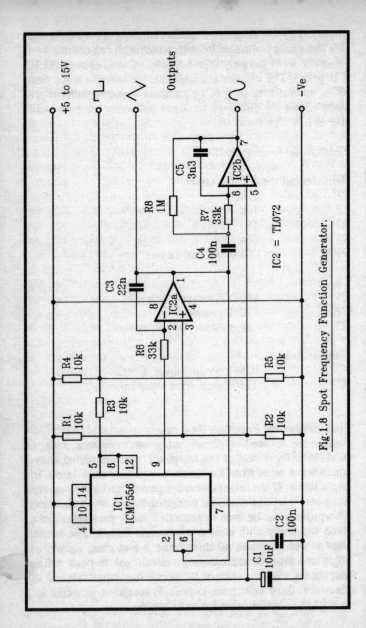

Fig.1.8 Spot Frequency Function Generator.

22

The circuit is shown in Figure 1.8. The dual timer IC1 and the integrator IC2a generate the square and triangle waves in the same manner as the earlier circuit, but with one small difference. An aim of this design was to generate all three outputs with roughly the same output voltage for use in rapid testing of the response of other circuits to the different waveforms. The triangle wave sets the initial value, with its peak-to-peak voltage of one-third of the supply. The squarewave initially has a value of the supply voltage as it swings from rail to rail, but it is then attenuated by the two resistors R4 and R5 to approximately the desired value. If it is not required these two resistors can be omitted.

The triangle wave is connected to the input of IC2b, a second integrator. Without some form of DC feedback the output of an integrator will eventually drift as far as it can towards one of the supply rails due to input offset voltages and currents, etc., so IC2b is AC coupled to the input signal through C4 and the high value feedback resistor, R8, maintains the correct DC output level. The values of these two component are high enough to avoid distortion of the signal at the operating frequency. The output amplitude is set by the values of R7 and C5 to the required level of about a third of the supply peak-to-peak. The frequency is calculated, as with the earlier circuit, from:

$$f = \frac{1}{1.333 \times R6 \times C5}$$

A surprisingly good sinewave can be generated in this way, the only drawback being that the frequency cannot easily be adjusted. Any alteration of the input frequency to the second integrator will require adjustment of the values of R7 and C5 to maintain the correct sinewave output amplitude, and there is no simple way of doing this. Would that there were such a way! Most circuits capable of producing variable frequency sinewave outputs are fairly complex, but they will be covered later in this book. Meanwhile there are many applications for which a fixed frequency sinewave signal source is useful, and this simple circuit should be sufficient for most of them.

*Components for Figure 1.8*

*Resistors* (all metal film, 0.6W)
| | |
|-----|------|
| R1 | 10k |
| R2 | 10k |
| R3 | 10k |
| R4 | 10k |
| R5 | 10k |
| R6 | 33k |
| R7 | 33k |
| R8 | 1M |

*Capacitors*
| | |
|-----|---------------------------------|
| C1 | 10μF/25V electrolytic |
| C2 | 100nF ceramic |
| C3 | 22nF polyester or polystyrene |
| C4 | 100nF polyester or polystyrene |
| C5 | 3n3 polyester or polystyrene |

*Semiconductors*
| | |
|------|------------------------------------|
| IC1 | ICM7556 dual timer, CMOS |
| IC2 | TL072 dual JFET input op-amp. |

## Voltage Controlled Oscillator With 50:50 Duty Cycle

This, the last circuit of this chapter, is the most complex of the voltage-controlled oscillators to be shown in this section, incorporating some techniques that may prove useful to circuit designers in other applications. Unlike the circuits shown in Figures 1.4 and 1.5 which had pulse outputs, it provides both squarewave and triangle-wave outputs with 50:50 duty cycles. This can be useful in many applications, especially in audio. The frequency is controlled by a voltage which is referenced to the negative supply voltage.

The circuit is shown in Figure 1.9. The first two op-amps, IC1a and IC1b, act as a voltage level-shifter for converting an input that is referenced to the negative supply into one that is referenced to half the supply voltage. It works as follows. IC1a biases the transistor TR1 so that the control voltage, Vin, appears across the resistor R1. Nearly all the resulting current through this resistor reappears at the collector of TR1, so this

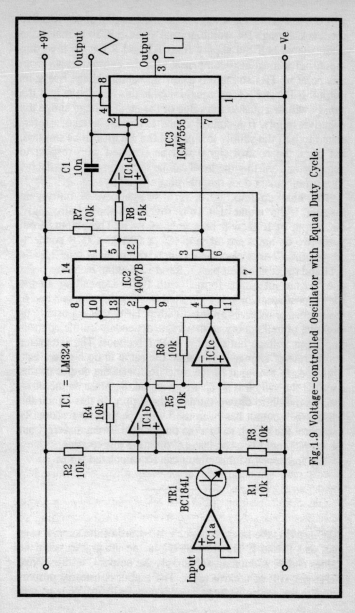

Fig.1.9 Voltage-controlled Oscillator with Equal Duty Cycle.

25

part of the circuit is a voltage-controlled current sink. Negative feedback through R4 would normally cause IC2b to match the reference of half the supply from R2 and R3 at its inverting input, but it must also compensate for the current drawn from this point by TR1 so there is a corresponding voltage rise at its output. If R1 and R4 are equal in value this rise above half the supply will be equal to the value of the input voltage above the negative supply. If a control signal is already available referenced to half the supply this part of the circuit can be omitted, but often the control signal will be supplied with respect to negative and shifting the level can be something of a headache. This arrangement does the job most efficiently.

The next op-amp, IC1c, is a straightforward unity-gain inverter. If the output of IC1b is, say, a volt above half-supply, the output of IC1c will be a volt below it. The outputs from these two op-amps are taken to IC2, a CMOS 4007B connected to form a 2-way electronic switch with poles at pins 2,9 and 4,11 and the common at pins 1, 5 and 12. Output from this point goes to the integrator formed with IC1d. Depending on the switch position, which is controlled by the level at pins 3 and 6, the integrator receives an input with polarity that is positive or negative of half supply, with a value dependant on the controlling input voltage but equal in both directions. The integrator output rate of change is therefore the same in both directions. This goes to the input of the timer IC3, and the output of this controls the switch IC2, changeovers taking place as the input reaches one-third or two-thirds of the supply. In this circuit the "discharge" output has been used with the pull-up resistor R7 to control the switch so that the output of IC3 remains free, but the output could be used instead, omitting this resistor.

The frequency of this circuit can be calculated from:

$$f = \frac{E}{2 \times V \times R \times C}$$

Where E is the input voltage, V is a third of the supply voltage, and R and C are R8 and C1 in the integrator. With the values shown and a nine-volt supply the output is a little above 1kHz per volt of control input. The output is linearly proportional to the control voltage, but of course will also change with

26

supply voltage variations unless the input is a proportion of the supply.

The op-amps in the test circuit were the four contained in a single LM324 package. Using these, the circuit worked up to around 10kHz before distortion of the triangle-wave became pronounced. Replacing the integrator op-amp IC1d with a TL071 improved high frequency performance, and with a 100pF capacitor for C1 it then worked reasonably well to above 100kHz. At the other end of the range, it can run practically as slowly as the designer needs. Frequencies well below 1Hz are perfectly feasible. Op-amp IC1a must be a type that can operate with inputs and output at negative supply potential, and the input should not be more than about a quarter of the supply to allow sufficient working "headroom" for TR1. The squarewave output is available from pin 3 of IC3, and a triangle-wave output, with peak-to-peak amplitude of a third of the supply, can be taken from the output of IC1d.

*Components for Figure 1.9*

*Resistors* (all metal film, 0.6W)

| | |
|-----|-----|
| R1 | 10k |
| R2 | 10k |
| R3 | 10k |
| R4 | 10k |
| R5 | 10k |
| R6 | 10k |
| R7 | 10k |
| R8 | 15k |

*Capacitors*

| | |
|----|------------------------------|
| C1 | 10n polyester or polystyrene |

*Semiconductors*

| | |
|-----|---------------------------------------------------------|
| IC1 | LM324 Quad op-amp. |
| IC2 | CMOS, 4007B, dual complementary pair plus inverter. |
| IC3 | ICM7555 timer, CMOS |
| TR1 | BC184L |

# Chapter 2

## CMOS RESISTOR CAPACITOR OSCILLATORS

### Basic CMOS R-C Oscillator

CMOS devices offer a lot of scope to designers of R-C oscillators. Circuits can be constructed both from basic gates and with ICs designed especially for use in oscillator circuits. With inputs that operate around half the supply voltage and outputs that can swing all the way to both positive and negative supply potentials, CMOS gates are ideally suited to stable oscillator design. Circuits using them are often simpler and more reliable than equivalent designs based on discrete devices such as transistors, and have largely replaced these in modern design. Their low power requirement and supply voltage range of 3 to 15 volts also makes them ideal for use in battery-powered circuits. There are some pitfalls however, which should be understood and these will be fully explained in this chapter.

The basic requirement for most R-C oscillator circuits is a pair of inverters connected in series as shown in Figure 2.1. Assuming that the input is to gate G1, both inverted and non-inverted outputs are simultaneously available, from G1 and G2 respectively. The oscillator action is easy to follow. If it is assumed that the output from G1 is at the instant of going positive, the resulting positive input to G2 will cause the output of this to go negative and this negative signal will be passed through capacitor C1 and resistor R1 back to the input of G1, accelerating the action until a complete change of state of both gates has taken place. The positive output from G1 will then commence charging C1, gradually raising the voltage at G1 input. When it reaches half the supply voltage G1's output will again begin to change state, this time to negative, and the whole cycle will repeat.

The time required for each half-cycle is $1.1 \times R \times C$, so the frequency is given by:

$$f = \frac{1}{2.2 \times R \times C}$$

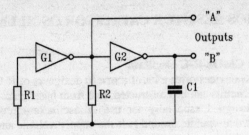

2.1a. Basic CMOS C-R Oscillator.

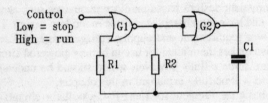

2.1b. "NOR" gate oscillator

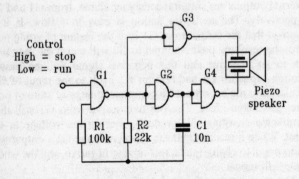

2.1c. "NAND" gate oscillator

Fig.2.1. Basic CMOS C-R Oscillator Circuits

where R is R2 and C is C1 in the circuit shown.

Suitable values for resistor R2 are from about 10k upwards, and for capacitor C1 from 100pF upwards. As the voltage polarity across C2 is reversed every half-cycle this component cannot be a polarised type such as an electrolytic, but most other types can be used. For good stability polystyrene and polyester capacitors are recommended.

Two outputs are available, one from each gate. Either or both can be used. They are opposite in phase, a feature which is often useful in circuit designs. As with the basic circuits of chapter 1 the frequency can be adjusted by using a variable resistor for R2, and the duty cycle can be altered by using combinations of diodes and resistors. Once again, it is the period that is controlled by this resistor, so the frequency control action will be non-linear.

Although it is simple and reliable, there are some potential pitfalls with this circuit which users should be aware of. Firstly, the output duty cycle is rarely quite even. For an exact 50:50 ratio or a very low frequency, see the next circuit in this chapter which uses a divider IC. Secondly, up to about 10kHz the output frequency generally conforms to the above formula but beyond this it becomes less predictable, usually being lower than calculations suggest. The frequency is also sensitive to supply voltage changes, generally increasing slightly as the voltage rises, and again this effect becomes more noticeable at high frequencies. CMOS gates are well-known for their low supply current requirements but this only applies when their inputs spend most of the time close to the supply rails. With intermediate input voltages their output stages can become partially conductive. Since the input to G1 changes relatively slowly, this gate draws current for part of each cycle. This is not usually a problem as with most gate types it involves only a few hundred microamps, but some of the high-current inverting buffers are not recommended for this type of circuit as they can draw sufficient current to overheat! Another effect of the slowly-rising input to G1 is instability and "glitches", or spikes, around the switching points. Often invisible unless viewed on a fast oscilloscope, this can produce unpredictable effects if the signal is used, for example, to drive a counter. This problem can often be cured simply by putting a 10k resistor in series with the drive to the counter. With the counter's input capacitance, this forms a low-pass filter which is usually sufficient to fix the problem. Another approach would be the use of "Schmitt" gates, such as those of the 4093B quad Schmitt NAND, but the hysteresis of these will affect the frequency calculations and also increase frequency shifts with variations in supply voltage. The use of Schmitt gates does not cure the current consumption problem either.

These factors should not discourage designers from using this type of oscillator though, as it is simple, cheap and reliable and in most applications it operates without problems. So long as the potential pitfalls are understood, the cause of unexpected effects can usually be readily found and eliminated.

The purpose of resistor R1 is worth an explanation as it is not always understood. At the instant when the output of G2 starts to change state, let's say to positive, the side of capacitor C1 facing the input of G1 is at half the supply voltage. As G2's output switches, this side is raised initially to one and a half times the supply voltage. The same thing happens for negative output changes, only in the opposite direction with the input to G1 dropping to half the supply voltage below negative rail. Most B-series CMOS devices contain internal circuitry designed to protect their inputs from such voltages to prevent static discharge damage. This protection takes various forms depending on the manufacturer, but usually consists of diode networks arranged to conduct if voltages above or below the supplies are connected to them. In the R-C oscillator circuit this would result in rapid initial discharge of C1 whilst its voltage exceeded the supplies. This would adversely affect performance and stability so R1 restricts current flow into the protection, greatly reducing the effect. The value of this resistor should be reasonably high in comparison with R2, generally a ratio of four to one or greater is sufficient.

Although Figure 2.1a shows a circuit using two simple inverters, it can be built with NOR or NAND gates as shown in Figure 2.1b and 2.1c, which use gates from a 4001B and 4011B respectively. Surplus inputs can be connected together, or to positive supply, or they can be used as shown for controlling the oscillator. Where a four-gate IC is used the remaining gates can be used for a variety of purposes. Two oscillators could be built, one for audio frequency and the other operating at one or two hertz and gating the first to give a pulsed tone output. The spare gates could be used as buffers to prevent loading of the oscillator circuit. One useful suggestion is to use them for driving a piezo sounder device, using the two gates as buffers with opposite output polarities to create a "bridge" driver circuit. This is shown in Fig.2.1c with G3 and G4 as the buffers.

Most of the inverting CMOS gates can be used in this type of oscillator. Some suitable types are shown in the following list:

4000B  Dual 3-input NOR gate plus inverter
4001B  Quad 2-input NOR gate
4002B  Dual 4-input NOR gate
4011B  Quad 2-input NAND gate
4012B  Dual 4-input NAND gate
4023B  Triple 3-input NAND gate
4025B  Triple 3-input NOR gate
4093B  Quad 2-input Schmitt NAND gate.

It is also possible to use the 4070B quad EX-OR and 4077B quad EX-NOR devices, since these 2-input gates can be used as inverters if one of the inputs is connected to the appropriate supply voltage. With the 4070B this is positive, for the 4077B it is negative. Again, this provides an option to control the oscillation with these inputs.

*Components for Figure 2.1c*

*Resistors* (metal film, 0.6W)
R1                100k
R2                22k

*Capacitors*
C1                10n polyester

*Semiconductors*
IC1             4011B CMOS quad NAND gate

*Miscellaneous*
Piezo sounder

## CMOS 4060B 14-stage Ripple Counter
## with Internal Oscillator

A useful version of the basic oscillator can be found in the 4060B oscillator and divider IC. This is essentially a 14-stage binary counter-divider, but unlike the other ripple counters, a pair of inverters already connected for use as an oscillator lurks behind pins 9, 10 and 11. This can be used in various ways, the most basic being as a C-R oscillator as shown at the top of Figure 2.2. All the previous information about this type of oscillator is relevant to this, including the operating frequency which is given by the formula $f = 1/(2.2 \times R2 \times C1)$. R1 performs the same function as before and there are similar limitations on the maximum reliable frequency.

The input to the two gates, pin 11, is also internally connected to the "clock" input of the divider, giving some useful options. The output can be taken from any of the divider outputs. As they are multiples of complete oscillator cycles, all have perfect 50:50 duty cycles. They are buffered, so it is impossible to affect the oscillator frequency by loading them. They can even be used for directly driving low-current LEDs, which is sometimes of value for constructing very cheap counting or timing circuits. The division process makes this IC especially suitable for the construction of very low frequency oscillators using sensible values of resistance and capacitance. Sadly, the first three outputs are not available to the user. The first one externally available is output 4, at pin 7, which runs at 1/16th of the clock frequency. Even more of a disadvantage is the missing output 11, representing the clock divided by 2048. This gap in the sequence of outputs is often a real nuisance as this IC would otherwise be ideal for very simple binary "address" generation.

The "Reset" input, to pin 12, should be connected to negative supply for normal operation. If it is taken to the positive supply all the outputs will go low and remain there until the reset is returned to the low state and a clock input is applied. The oscillator outputs at pins 9 and 10 will also be low whilst the reset is active. This can be used to control the oscillator, or if the chip is being used to generate a binary output value, to reset this to zero and determine the starting time. Like all CMOS inputs, the reset pin should never be left unconnected as strange and

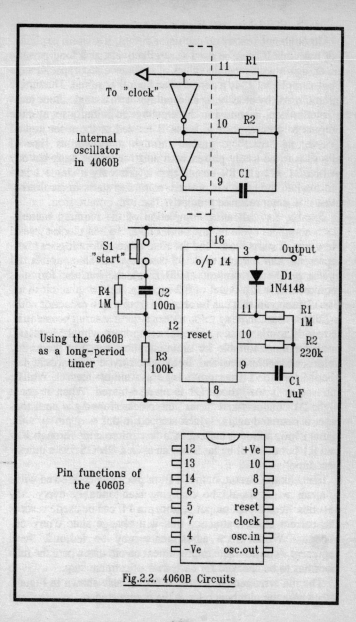

To "clock"

Internal
oscillator
in 4060B

11 — R1

10 — R2

9 — C1

S1
"start"

16

o/p 14

3 — Output

D1
1N4148

R4
1M

C2
100n

11 — R1
1M

12 — reset

10 — R2
220k

Using the 4060B
as a long-period
timer

R3
100k

9 — C1
1uF

8

Pin functions of
the 4060B

| | |
|---|---|
| 12 | +Ve |
| 13 | 10 |
| 14 | 8 |
| 6 | 9 |
| 5 | reset |
| 7 | clock |
| 4 | osc.in |
| -Ve | osc.out |

Fig.2.2. 4060B Circuits

unpredictable effects will result!

Although not strictly an oscillator circuit, it's worth explaining how this IC can be used very effectively as a long-period timer, again with sensible values of resistance and capacitance. For example, let's say a period of an hour is required. The timer circuit, made by modifying an oscillator with a single diode and a reset switch, is shown in the drawing. To initially set all the outputs to zero a positive pulse is needed at the reset input. Connecting "reset" to ground through a resistor as shown allows it to be easily pulsed with positive by the push-button switch S1. C2 and R4 ensure that it gets only a single brief pulse when the button is pressed, so timing starts immediately even if it is not released promptly. The 14th output, from pin 3, is suitable for indicating completion of the required period. Each complete cycle of this output takes 16,384 clock cycles. However, it starts "low" and the time taken before it goes high represents half a cycle, or 8,192 clock cycles. This number of cycles per hour represents 2.28Hz, which from the formula requires a C × R product of 0.2 seconds. This is quite close to the 0.22 seconds that can be obtained from a 1µF capacitor with a 220k resistor, making these values a good starting point. 1µF is readily available as a polyester component with a 5% tolerance, far more suitable for timing applications than the high-value, wide-tolerance and leaky electrolytic that would be needed for a 555 timer providing this kind of interval. Whilst the output is low, diode D1 is reverse-biased. When it goes high, D1 conducts and "jams" the clock, stopping it until the reset is operated again. Whilst stopped in this way pin 10 will remain low, taking a current of a few microamps through R2 and R1 but this will be far less than even a CMOS 555's quiescent supply.

To check the circuit, output 4 from pin 7 can be viewed with a meter as it should be changing state roughly every 3.5 seconds. To set it up, output 8, from pin 14, can be used, as with the correct clock frequency this will change state every 56 seconds. Whilst such adjustments may be tedious, they represent a considerable improvement on circuits where the full hour has to be checked for each trial adjustment step.

The pin arrangement for the 4060B is also shown in Figure 2.2, where the numbers refer to the output stages.

*Components for Figure 2.2*

*Resistors* (metal film, 0.6W)
R1, 4          1M (2 off)
R2             220k
R3             100k

*Capacitors*
C1             1µF polyester layer
C2             100n polyester or ceramic

*Semiconductors*
D1             1N4148 silicon signal diode
IC1            4060B CMOS 14-stage counter with internal
               oscillator

## CMOS 4016B Transmission Gate Oscillator

Another CMOS device that can be used to build a two-gate oscillator is the 4016B quad "analogue switch". This contains four electronic "switches", each of which can be "closed" by the application of a positive control voltage. If two of these are connected to form inverters, they can be used just like any other inverting gates to construct an oscillator. Figure 2.3a shows the pin connections for this IC. Note that, like other CMOS devices, unused inputs should be connected to either positive or negative supply, never left "floating". Figure 2.3b shows how a single switch can be arranged as an inverter. One side of the switch is connected to ground whilst the other is connected to the positive supply through a 10k resistor. Whilst the control input, labelled "in" in the drawing, is connected to a negative voltage the junction between the switch and resistor, labelled "out", is pulled up to positive by the resistor. When the input is supplied with a positive potential, the switch turns on and pulls the junction down to negative. Provided the resistor value is low enough in comparison with the load that the "gate" will be driving, the arrangement gives a performance similar to any other type of inverting gate.

For use as an oscillator two of these "inverting gates" are built using two of the four switches of IC1, and the usual oscillator

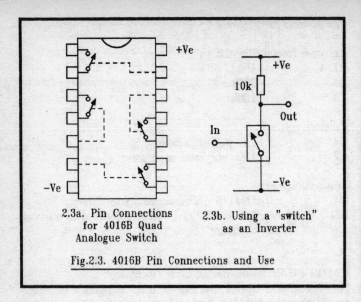

2.3a. Pin Connections
for 4016B Quad
Analogue Switch

2.3b. Using a "switch"
as an Inverter

Fig.2.3. 4016B Pin Connections and Use

components are added as shown in Figure 2.4a. Two outputs are available, labelled "A" and "B". These, when viewed on an oscilloscope, are rather "messy", with glitches and instability around the switching points, and the frequency that can be achieved with this circuit is fairly low, though perfectly adequate for audio applications. A small disadvantage of the circuit is that one or other of the gates is always in the "on" state, so there will be a continuous drain on the supply current through the associated load resistor.

Like the others, the frequency of this circuit can be calculated from the formula $f = 1/(2.2 \times R \times C)$. It departs from the calculated value more rapidly than most with increasing frequency, so calculation should be used only as a guide before practical testing when designing with it. To give some idea, the values shown should generate an output frequency of about 455Hz. In practice it ran at 430Hz, quite close to the calculated value. However, reducing the value of C1 to 100pF resulted in an output of only 24KHz, little more than half the calculated value. A 22pF capacitor connected across resistor R1 improved this to 39KHz so this may be worthwhile in some designs. The

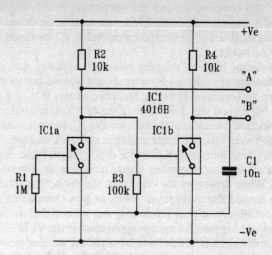

Fig.2.4a. 4016B Transmission Gate Oscillator

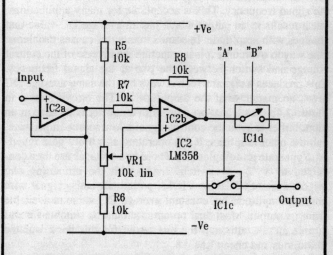

Fig.2.4b. Suggested Voltage−Controlled Audio Circuit

frequency of this circuit is fairly stable with changes in supply voltage and temperature and the duty-cycle of its output is reasonably close to a 50:50 ratio. As with most of the other two-gate circuits, this can be altered by replacing R3 by diode and resistor networks.

This circuit is slow, requires two extra resistors and may draw more supply current. So why should anyone bother constructing an oscillator from the switches in this IC? Just one reason, but a good one. Like most of the of the other oscillators of this section it uses a single inexpensive IC, but this time the "gates left over" are two spare analogue switches, and with two opposite-phase outputs available for driving them these can be used in all sorts of ingenious ways, including as a two-way switch. When driven by the oscillator, they reject the glitches present around the changeover points to give clean operation, and in addition to digital levels they can control DC voltages and analogue signals. An sample application is shown in Figure 2.4b. Earlier circuits in this book have shown ways of generating a signal with voltage-controlled amplitude by switching between the negative supply and a variable control voltage at the signal frequency. This is acceptable for many applications, but it results in an output which has an average DC value that changes with amplitude. In some circuits this causes problems. One way to overcome it is to generate the inverse of the control voltage and switch between the two at the signal frequency. This produces a signal which always has the same average DC level, no matter what the amplitude is. The circuit shown in Figure 2.4b uses a dual op-amp, with amplifier IC2a used as an input buffer to give the control signal a low source impedance, and the other amplifier, IC2b, operating as a unity-gain inverter to generate its complement. These two voltages are then connected to a "2-way switch" made with the remaining two 4016B switches IC1c and IC1d, so that an audio signal with varying amplitude but constant average DC value is available from its output. Most dual op-amps should be suitable for this simple circuit, although the one tested for this book was the ubiquitous and cheap LM358.

Despite its simplicity this circuit has excellent performance and the uses are limited only by the designer's imagination. For starters, how about an output stage for detecting "null" in a DC bridge circuit? The pot VR1 shown in the circuit can be used to offset any quiescent voltage so that any change in the DC input, positive or negative, will be immediately audible. Since the ear has a logarithmic response a very large dynamic range will be covered, with excellent sensitivity at low levels.

*Components for Figure 2.4*

*Resistors* (all metal film, 0.6W)
R1                      1M
R2, 4, 5, 6, 7, 8   10k (6 off)
R3                      100k
VR1                    10k linear pot, carbon.

*Capacitors*
C1                      10n

*Semiconductors*
IC1                     4016B CMOS quad analogue switch
IC2                     LM358 dual op-amp.

## CMOS 4047B Astable Oscillator

This is a little different to the preceding ICs in that it is purpose-designed to be used as a versatile timer and oscillator. As such, it is capable of much better performance and higher frequencies. Whilst oscillators are often conjured up out of a few spare gates from ICs used in performing other circuit functions, when the designer wants to create an oscillator from scratch or needs improved performance this IC may be the best choice. Various pin connections allow it to be used in various configurations such as a monostable timer with positive or negative triggering, complementary outputs and reset, or as an astable oscillator with two output modes.

The pin functions for the 4047B are shown in Figure 2.5, with the basic connections for using it as an oscillator. This uses just one capacitor and one resistor to set the frequency, which as before is determined from the formula $f = 1/(2.2 \times R \times C)$. R can have any value from 10k up to around 1M, whilst C should be greater than 100pF and must not be a polarised type.

41

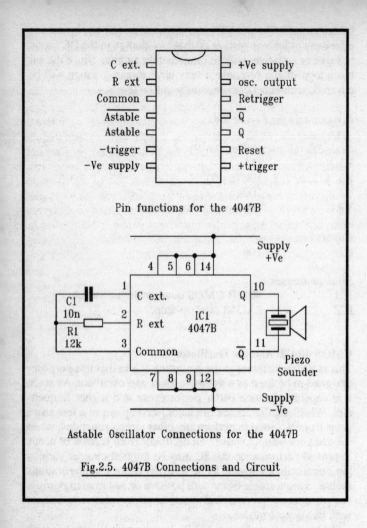

Pin functions for the 4047B

Astable Oscillator Connections for the 4047B

Fig.2.5. 4047B Connections and Circuit

Although the internal oscillator is still a two-gate circuit, the problem of the input protection diodes has been eliminated in this device so the usual series resistor to the input is unnecessary. This results in much better accuracy, especially at high frequencies.

When used as an oscillator three outputs are available. The first, "Osc out" is a buffered output operating at the basic oscillator frequency, available from pin 13. This is not guaranteed to have a perfect 50:50 duty cycle, but in practice it is generally much better than the simple two-gate circuits, especially at low frequencies. The other two outputs are "Q" and "$\overline{Q}$", from pins 10 and 11 respectively. These are provided from an internal single-stage divider circuit so they have perfect 50:50 duty cycles but run at half the primary oscillator frequency. They are buffered, and are complementary, so that whilst one is positive the other is negative. This has various uses, one of which could be driving a piezo sounder device placed across them to use them as a bridge output for greater volume. This works very well, producing quite a loud sound even from a 5-volt supply. The connections for this are shown in Figure 2.5, for an output frequency of about 1.9kHz, a suitable frequency for most piezo sounders.

The oscillator frequency is given by :

$$f = \frac{1}{2.2 \times R \times C}$$

but it should be remembered that only the output from pin 13 operates at this rate. The outputs from pins 10 and 11 run at half this frequency, so it can be calculated from:

$$f = \frac{1}{4.4 \times R \times C}$$

The performance of this device is generally much better than either simple two-gate circuits or the internal oscillator of the 4060B. At high frequencies the output corresponds much more closely to the calculated value. A test circuit using 100pF and 22k, for an output of 206kHz, actually produced 173kHz with a supply of 10 volts, comparing very favourably with the 4060B which managed only 100kHz under the same conditions. Variation with supply voltage is less too, at 5 volts this circuit still managed to run at 155kHz. If a reasonably stable C-R oscillator operating up to 100kHz is required, this IC is probably the best choice.

The "reset" input, pin 9, can be used to control the "Q" and "Q̄" outputs. Normally this input should be kept low, or negative. When connected to positive it forces "Q" low and "Q̄" high. It does not stop the oscillator however, this continues to operate and the signal from the "osc. out" pin 13 will still be present. If zero power consumption is required whilst the oscillator is not running, this is not the way to stop this one! Another way to stop it is to take pin 5, "astable", low. This does stop the oscillator, with "osc" and "Q" low and "Q̄" high. This prevents the device from drawing any supply current at all, which may be necessary in some designs.

*Components for Figure 2.5*

*Resistors*
R1              12k

*Capacitors*
C1              10n

*Semiconductors*
IC1             4047B CMOS, timer/oscillator.

*Miscellaneous*
Piezo sounder.

## CMOS 4046B Voltage-Controlled Oscillator

A completely different type of oscillator circuit is to be found within the 4046B "phase-locked loop" IC. This versatile device has, amongst other things, a voltage-controlled oscillator that is exceptionally easy to use. Unfortunately descriptions of this are frequently difficult to follow, especially as it has two separate external frequency control connections. It is actually quite simple to work with, as this section will explain. However, there are some inherent problems with this device that may exclude it from many designs and these will also be described in detail.

The basic connections for the oscillator are shown in Figure 2.6, which includes a greatly simplified version of its internal structure. The frequency is set by an external capacitor C1

44

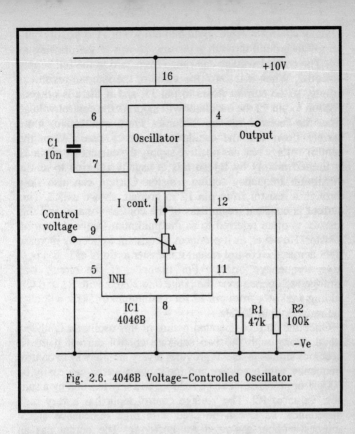

Fig. 2.6. 4046B Voltage–Controlled Oscillator

connected between pins 6 and 7 and is controlled by a current, the value of which is set externally by the connections to pins 9, 11 and 12. The capacitor can have any value from 50pF upwards, but must not be a polarised type as the internal circuit operates by alternately grounding each end whilst charging the other to half the supply voltage. The component values shown are for an output frequency of about 2 to 6kHz.

There are two separate paths through which the circuit designer can set the oscillator control current, and it is not necessary to use them both. Usually the main one is through pin 11. Control current flows from the oscillator to this pin through an internal voltage controlled resistor, whose value is set by an

45

external control voltage applied to pin 9. Pin 11 is usually connected to ground through a resistor, shown in the drawing as R1. The control voltage can range from zero to the full supply potential. When it is zero, the value of the internal resistor is infinity so no current flows to pin 11, and if there is no connection to pin 12 the oscillator will stop. As the control voltage rises the internal resistor becomes more conductive, more current flows and the oscillator frequency rises. When the control voltage reaches positive supply the current from pin 11 is limited mainly by R1 so this is usually referred to as the maximum frequency setting resistor. Current can also flow through a resistor from pin 12 to ground, shown as R2. This current is constant, regardless of the control voltage, and this resistor is often referred to as the minimum frequency setting resistor. However, as it produces a constant frequency increase right across the control range, it is easier to think of it as a positive frequency "offset". For instance, if the circuit was arranged to operate over the range 0 to 20kHz with R1 and C1, adding a resistor from pin 12 for a minimum of 5kHz will alter the range to 5 to 25kHz.

Once the current-operated nature of this oscillator is understood, along with the two separate control current paths, it becomes simple to use. It provides a very simple way to control frequency with a voltage and the range covered can easily be 1000:1 or more, or it can be reduced to a tiny fraction by a suitable value of R2. The voltage control input has a very high impedance, so it can be used with high impedance signal sources without the need for buffering. The output has an excellent 50:50 duty cycle, and the maximum frequency can be set easily from sub-audio to 2 or 3MHz. The output frequency is reasonably linear with the control voltage, although there is some deviation below about 20% of the supply. It can also be stopped and started simply by pin 5, the "inhibit" input. This should normally be connected to negative but making it positive will stop the oscillator.

Unfortunately there is a downside with this IC as it has some significant problems relating to stability and variation between devices. These unfortunately exclude it from many applications for which it might at first sight appear ideal. By far the greatest problem is lack of stability with changes in supply voltage. For example, a trial circuit configured to run at 10kHz with a supply of 15 volts dropped to 6.8kHz at 10 volts and just 2.1kHz at 5 volts. This indicates that in practical use this IC will nearly always need a regulated supply voltage and performance is much reduced at 5 volts, limiting its usefulness in battery circuits. One possibility would be to regulate to 5 volts and then use an ICM7660 voltage doubler to give a stable 10 volt supply, but this would wipe out the benefits of simplicity and low cost. A random selection of six 4046B's tried in the same circuit yielded frequencies from 9.9kHz to 12.7kHz, suggesting that many applications would need pre-set or "select-on-test" adjustment for correct operation. There is also a slight sensitivity to temperature change, a burst of freezer spray causes a typical variation of around 2%.

The wide variation of frequency with voltage makes it difficult to offer a formula for choosing R and C, but with a supply of 10 volts a reasonable starting point would be:

$$f = \frac{2}{C \times R}$$

followed by some practical testing to determine the exact values needed. This formula applies to both pins 11 and 12, in the case of pin 11 it assumes full positive supply voltage at pin 9. For half the supply voltage the frequency will be about half this value. The resistors from pins 11 and 12 to negative should be in the range of 10k to 1M.

Although it is usual to operate this IC with a resistor from pin 11 as the main frequency-setting component, it is quite possible to leave this pin unconnected and use only a resistor from pin 12 to set a fixed frequency. It is then possible to use a much higher value resistor from pin 11 to ground to provide a very small voltage controlled range of adjustment. This is not always obvious in descriptions of this IC, but it is worth knowing because it could find some useful applications.

*Components for Figure 2.6*

*Resistors* (all metal film, 0.6W)
R1                47k

| R2 | 100k |
|---|---|

*Capacitors*

| C1 | 10n polyester or polystyrene. |
|---|---|

*Semiconductors*

| IC1 | 4046B CMOS "phase-locked loop". |
|---|---|

## White Noise Generator

Considering that noise is a major problem in many areas of electronics, it comes as something of a surprise to discover that when some is needed, it is quite difficult to find a good source. Zener diodes are widely regarded as being "noisy", but in practice most generate only microvolts. The base-emitter junction of a transistor, if reverse-biased into breakdown, will sometimes produce quite a lot of noise but the effect is unpredictable and therefore not suitable for use in reliable circuit designs. Special "noise diodes" were once available, but the manufacture of these seems to have been discontinued for some time now. So, if a designer needs a good noise signal for testing or the creation of sound effects, how can it be generated?

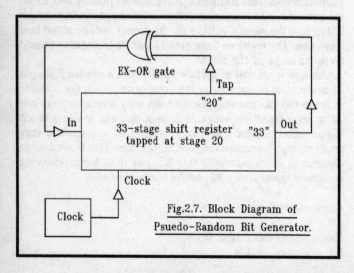

Fig.2.7. Block Diagram of
Psuedo-Random Bit Generator.

48

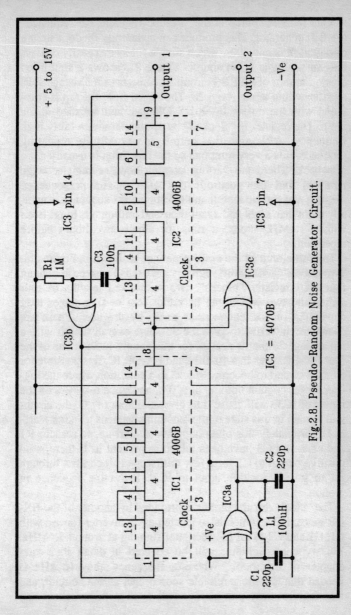

Fig.2.8. Pseudo-Random Noise Generator Circuit.

49

One reliable source is the "Pseudo-Random Bit sequence" (PRBS) generator. This produces an apparently random stream of digital "1"s and "0"s, which simple filters can easily convert into an analogue noise source. Figure 2.7 shows a simplified block diagram of a PRBS circuit. It consists of a 33-stage shift register with a tap at stage 20. The signal from the tap is combined with the output in an EX-OR gate and returned to the input. The register is "clocked" by an oscillator at a fairly high frequency. Although the output is actually a repeating sequence, it is a very long one so the repetition is usually not a drawback. There are various combinations of register stage numbers and tap positions that give maximum sequence lengths, and for the length and tap shown the sequence is actually more than eight and a half thousand million bits long! Even with a 1.4MHz clock, it runs for almost two hours before repetition.

The full circuit of the noise generator is shown in Figure 2.8. Two 4006B CMOS shift registers are used. These each contain four shift register "blocks", two with fixed lengths of four stages and two which can be either four or five stages long depending on the connections made by the user. These are connected in series to give the 33-stage overall length with a tap at stage 20 that is needed for this circuit. IC3b is one of the four EX-OR gates in a 4070B quad EX-OR IC. It is possible for a PRBS circuit to become "stuck" in a condition where the register stages contain nothing but "0"s, and since two "0"s on the inputs of IC3b will cause it to give an output of "0" the circuit will remain in this state until something happens to "kick-start" it. Unfortunately this often happens on start-up, so resistor R1 and capacitor C3 have been added to prevent it. If there is no positive output to C3 for a few milliseconds it charges through R1 to give a positive input to IC3b to set the sequence in motion.

The "clock" for the circuit is provided by another of the EX-OR gates, IC3a, which is connected as an inverter for use with L1, C1 and C2 as an LC oscillator running at around 1.4MHz. This type of oscillator will be covered in detail in a later chapter of this book. Where a frequency above100kHz is needed this is a more reliable source than an R-C circuit, and also requires only one gate. It will work with just about any inductor of the right value, the one used in the test circuit was a tiny wire-ended 100µH choke. These are physically very similar to resistors and are just as easy to use. The output of IC3a drives the clock inputs of both shift register ICs.

The output is taken from stage 33 of the register, pin 9 of IC2. With some filtering, white noise is very useful for the creation of sound effects such as wind, surf, rushing water and so on, and in many instances these effects will be required in stereo. The second output for this can be tapped if necessary with a third EX-OR gate, IC3c, which combines outputs taken from two other points in the circuit. Although the two outputs are obviously related, in practice they don't sound as if though they are and they can be used to create excellent stereo effects.

This circuit works well with supplies from 5 to 15 volts and draws very little supply current, so it is ideal for use with battery operated projects. The output amplitude depends, of course, directly on the supply voltage. If no other use is found for it, the inputs to the fourth EX-OR gate should be tied to positive or negative supply, not left floating. For most applications some filtering of the output of this circuit will be needed, so this will be covered next.

*Components for Figure 2.8*

*Resistors*
R1                    1M (metal film, 0.6W)

*Capacitors*
C1, 2                 220pF ceramic or polystyrene (2 off)
C3                    100nF ceramic or polystyrene

*Inductor*
L1                    100µH miniature wire-ended choke.

*Semiconductors*
IC1, 2                4006B CMOS 18-stage serial-in, serial-out
                      shift register (2 off)
IC3                   4070B CMOS quad EX-OR

51

## Filtering and "Pink Noise"

Most applications for the PRBS white noise generator will need some filtering of its output. Figure 2.9 shows two filters that can be used. The simplest is a low-pass filter consisting of just a resistor and capacitor, as shown in Figure 2.9a, which will usually be sufficient. This attenuates the higher frequencies present in the signal above a "breakpoint" where the capacitive reactance is equal to the resistance. With the component values shown this is about 20kHz. It reduces the output level slightly, with a 10 volt supply the measured output is about 0.7V RMS. Larger values of capacitance can be used to give a "deeper" sound, like surf for instance. If the output level becomes too low it can be boosted with the op-amp circuit shown in Figure 2.9c, perhaps with some adjustment of the value of R2 to alter the gain. The voltage gain is given by:

$$G_v = \frac{(R2 + R1)}{R1}$$

Some test applications need a source of "pink noise", and it has to be said that this also sounds quite pleasant. "Pink" noise requires slightly more complex filtering than the simple type shown in figure 2.9a as it has to attenuate the higher frequencies by only 3dB per octave instead of the 6dB per octave of the simpler circuit. The arrangement shown in Figure 2.9b gives a reasonably close approximation to pink noise, using a series of four "breakpoints". The output from this filter is rather low at just 40mV RMS, and it should also not be unduly loaded as this could affect the filtering characteristic. The simple amplifier circuit of Figure 2.9c will boost it back up to 400mV RMS and also buffer it, so that it can be connected directly to most loads. The op-amp shown is a TL071 but for stereo applications the dual version of this, the TL072, could be used instead.


*Components for Figure 2.9a*

*Resistors*
R1                          22k (metal film, 0.6W)

52

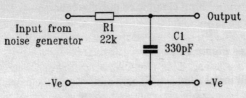

Fig.2.9a. Simple Low-pass Filter.

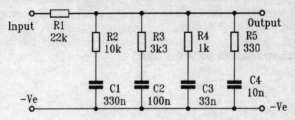

Fig.2.9b. "Pink Noise" Filter.

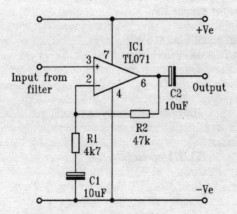

Fig.2.9c. Buffer Amplifier for Filters.

Fig.2.9. Filtering for White Noise Generator.

*Capacitors*
C1                330pF ceramic or polystyrene.


*Components - Figure 2.9b*

*Resistors* (all metal film, 0.6W)
R1           22k
R2           10k
R3           3k3
R4           1k
R5           330 ohm

*Capacitors* (all 5% polyester layer)
C1           330n
C2           100n
C3           33n
C4           10n


*Components for Figure 2.9c*

*Resistors* (all metal film, 0.6W)
R1           4k7
R2           47k

*Capacitors*
C1, 2         10μF/25V electrolytic (2 off)

*Semiconductors*
IC1           TL071 op-amp.

# Chapter 3

# OP-AMP RESISTOR CAPACITOR OSCILLATORS

## The Basic Op-amp R-C Oscillator

Like other active devices, op-amps can be used in the construction of oscillators. The simplest circuit has a "squarewave" output, uses only a few passive components in addition to the amplifier, and is very easy to design. Figure 3.1 shows two versions, for dual and single power supplies. The single-supply version has the advantage that for low frequencies the capacitor C1 can be an electrolytic type, though in most cases the capacitor of the split-supply version could be returned to the negative supply instead of ground.

The working of this oscillator is easier to follow from the dual-supply version of Figure 3.1a. In normal operation the output of the op-amp, $V_{out}$, is always as far as it can swing towards one of the supply rails. This places a voltage of R1/(R1+R2) × $V_{out}$ on the non-inverting input whilst the capacitor C1 charges towards that voltage through R3. When it reaches it the output changes state, with a rapid switching action ensured by positive feedback through R2. The capacitor then starts charging in the opposite direction and this action repeats at a frequency determined by the resistors and capacitors used.

To simplify frequency calculations for this circuit a couple of assumptions can be made. The first is that if dual supplies are used, the positive and negative voltages are equal, or if a single supply is used the resistors R1a and R1b are equal in value. In practice this will normally be the case. The second assumption is that the output of the op-amp can swing all the way to both supply rails. With a few exceptions this is not so, but it simplifies the calculation and provides an adequate starting point for practical experiments. The formula for frequency can then be calculated from:

$$f = \frac{1}{2 \times ln\left(1 - \frac{2 \times R1}{(2 \times R1) + R2}\right)} \times \frac{1}{R3 \times C1}$$

This is a lot to punch into a calculator, even assuming that it has the exponential function "ln" in its repertoire, so two much simpler versions are as follows. In many cases R1 will be equal to R2, and the frequency is then given by:

$$f = \frac{0.455}{R3 \times C1}$$

For the single-supply version, "R1" is the value of R1a and R1b in parallel. These will usually have the same value so it will be half the value of one of them. If equal value resistors are used for R1a, R1b and R2, "R1" will be half the value of R2 so the formula then becomes:

$$f = \frac{0.721}{R3 \times C1}$$

These two formulae provide a quick and simple estimate of the component values needed for most applications of this circuit. Its performance depends to a great extent on the bandwidth of the op-amp used. Slow types can only be used at low frequencies and even here the slow rise and fall times of the output may be a disadvantage. The outputs of many op-amps can get closer to one supply voltage than the other, causing non-symmetrical output, whilst the inability to swing all the way to one or both rails leads to deviation from the calculated frequency value. A few types may prove to be unstable in this circuit. The TLOxxx series of devices are stable and have outputs that, although not rail-to rail, have symmetrical offsets at either end. Most also have a good frequency response. A TLO71 tested in the circuit of Figure 3.1b gave 1.013kHz, and the variation with supply voltage from 5 to 25 volts was less than 1%. With a 1n capacitor, for 10.6kHz, it gave 9.97kHz and with 100pF the output was 77kHz. The JFET inputs of this device also make it suitable for very low frequencies using high values of resistor R3.

One of the best op-amps to use in this circuit is the 3130E. This is a CMOS device with very high input impedances and an output that, if lightly loaded, can swing all the way to both supply rails. In this application the usual frequency compensa-

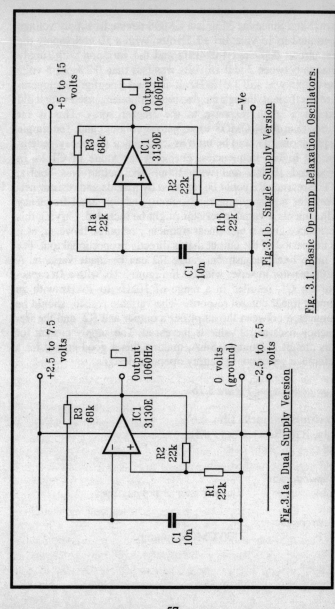

**Fig. 3.1. Basic Op-amp Relaxation Oscillators.**

Fig.3.1b. Single Supply Version

+5 to 15 volts

Output 1060Hz

−Ve

R3 68k

IC1 3130E

R2 22k

R1a 22k

R1b 22k

C1 10n

Fig.3.1a. Dual Supply Version

+2.5 to 7.5 volts

Output 1060Hz

0 volts (ground)

−2.5 to 7.5 volts

R3 68k

IC1 3130E

R2 22k

R1 22k

C1 10n

tion is not needed, indeed it would merely slow the output switching. Since the 3130 is a CMOS device its supply voltage is limited to 15 volts or ±7.5 volts. With a 10 volt supply the test circuit delivered 1.024kHz and the variation with supply change between 7 and 15 volts was less than 0.2%. At 5 volts the output was still 1.016kHz. It also had a negligible temperature coefficient, though the passive components used with it did exhibit a small response to the freezer spray. This is far better than most CMOS logic gate oscillators and, for simple applications, it could be used as a reference frequency generator. At higher frequencies, changing the value of C1 to 1n produced 10kHz, and with 100pF the output was 86kHz.

The resistor R3 could be replaced by a diode and resistor network for a non-symmetrical output, and for small frequency adjustments a variable resistor might be included. Varying this resistance gives a non-linear frequency response however, as it is the period of the output that is directly proportional to it. For a more linear adjustment range R2 can be made variable. A 220k resistor in series with R2 in Figure 3.1b, with a 1n capacitor for C1, resulted in a range of 10kHz to 75kHz with an almost linear control response. The variable resistor should be connected between the amplifier's output and R2, and the frequency rises as its value is increased. The supply current for this circuit is around 0.8mA, making this a good choice for a reference generator in battery operated designs.

*Components for Figure 3.1b*

*Resistors* (all metal film, 0.6W)
R1a, R1b, R2    22k (3 off)
R3              68k

*Capacitors*
C1              10n polyester or polystyrene

*Semiconductors*
IC1             3130 CMOS op-amp.

## Triangle and Squarewave Oscillators

This is the equivalent of the integrator and comparator circuits shown in Figures 1.6 and 1.7. The performance is not usually quite as good because of the inability of most op-amp outputs to swing all the way to the supply rails, but it can be constructed using one of the many cheap dual op-amps available with very few additional passive components, so there will be occasions where it is useful.

Figure 3.2a shows a simple fixed frequency circuit. IC1a is the integrator, whilst the comparator is IC1b with the level of hysteresis set by the ratio of resistors R2 and R3. When the output of the comparator is positive, current flowing into R1 causes IC1a's output to ramp towards negative at a rate set by R1 and C1. This output is connected to R2, the input to the comparator. When it is low enough, IC1b changes state and the change of polarity to R1 starts the integrator output ramping in the opposite direction. Two outputs are available, a triangle wave from the output of IC1a and a squarewave from the output of IC1b.

The frequency is given by:

$$f = \frac{R3}{4 \times R1 \times R2 \times C1}$$

and the triangle peak-to-peak amplitude is:

$$\frac{R2}{R3 \times V}$$

This assumes that the op-amp outputs can swing rail-to-rail, which will not usually be the case, but it is simple and gives a useful starting point for practical design. Many op-amp outputs can get closer to one supply rail than the other so the voltage applied to R1 is slightly greater in one direction than the other, leading to slight loss of output symmetry but in many applications this will not be a problem. A 3130 CMOS op-amp could be used as the comparator to overcome this, but if two ICs are to be used the ICM7556 is usually a better choice as it has the hysteresis resistors built in.

Practical testing of this circuit with a TL072 yielded just over 1.1kHz. With a 100pF capacitor for C1 it managed 72kHz,

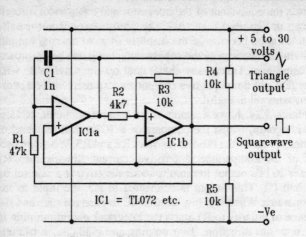

Fig.3.2a. Triangle-wave Oscillator.

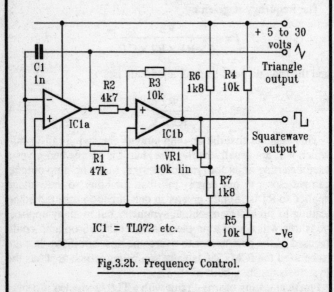

Fig.3.2b. Frequency Control.

60

and a TL082 was slightly faster at 79kHz. Stability with factors such as changing supply voltage was good. The frequency can be changed by altering any of the four passive components. It might be worth noting that the frequency is linearly proportional to the value of R3, so adjusting this gives a more linear range of control, but it also changes the amplitude of the triangle wave output. For reliable operation R3 should always be greater than 1.5 times the value of R2. Replacing R3 in Figure 3.2a with a 100k linear pot in series with an 8k2 resistor gave an adjustment range slightly greater than 1 to 10kHz.

For a reasonably linear frequency control with constant triangle wave amplitude, the modified circuit shown in Figure 3.2b can be used. This sends the output from IC1b to R1 through the variable attenuator VR1. The low end of this is given a half-supply potential by the divider resistors R6 and R7, with values chosen so that in parallel they represent slightly less than a tenth of the value of the pot. Unlike increasing the value of R3, which raises the frequency, this reduces it so C1 is reduced to 1n to obtain the same range of 1 to 10kHz.

Both circuits are shown for use with single supply voltages. Where a dual supply is available, R4 and R5 will be unnecessary, the two inputs they supply can be connected directly to ground, and the low end of VR1 can also be connected to ground, perhaps through a suitable resistor to set the minimum frequency.

*Components for Figures 3.2a and 3.2b*

*Resistors* (all metal film, 0.6W)

| | |
|---|---|
| R1 | 47k |
| R2 | 4k7 |
| R3, 4, 5 | 10k (3 off) |
| R6, 7 | 1k8 (2 off) |
| VR1 | 10k linear carbon pot |

*Capacitors*

| | |
|---|---|
| C1 | 10n or 1n polyester or polystyrene |

*Semiconductors*

| | |
|---|---|
| IC1 | TL072 |

## An Audio Sinewave Oscillator

Most of the oscillators described so far have been presented as simple outline circuits for use by designers and experimenters in their own projects. Extras such as power supply decoupling, output buffers and DC blocking capacitors have generally been omitted. However, this circuit can be constructed as an extremely useful general workshop test oscillator, so it is given as a complete mini-project. In Chapter 7, which deals with construction, full details are given for building it with a simple stripboard layout.

The design uses the "Wien Bridge" circuit to generate a sinewave output with excellent purity and it has four frequency ranges covering 10Hz to 100kHz. The output is from a 50-ohm source with an amplitude control for adjusting the level from zero to a maximum of 1 volt RMS, corresponding to about 2.8 volts peak-to-peak. The supply current is only about 12mA and a 9-volt supply can be used, making battery operation possible.

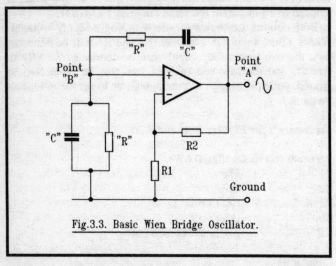

Fig.3.3. Basic Wien Bridge Oscillator.

The basic op-amp Wien Bridge oscillator circuit is shown in Figure 3.3. The bridge consists of two sections using the components "R" and "C", one with them in series, and the other with them in parallel. The junction of these two arms supplies positive feedback to the amplifier whilst negative feedback, for amplitude control, is applied through R2 and R1. The capacitors and resistors of a Wien Bridge are usually of equal value, so that when a sinewave is applied to the point "A" in the figure the feedback signal at point "B" will only be in phase with it at the frequency given by the formula:

$$f = \frac{1}{2 \times \pi \times R \times C}$$

This determines the frequency of oscillation since the positive feedback must be in phase for it to work. To allow variation of the output frequency the two resistors are often made variable by using a dual-ganged pot.

There's a snag to this delightfully simple circuit of course. Isn't there always? At the working frequency the positive feedback voltage at point "B" is exactly a third of that applied to point "A", so the amplifier must have a gain of exactly three to sustain the oscillation. The tiniest fraction more and the amplitude rises until the amplifier output "clips"; a tiny bit less and the oscillation simply dies away. This means that automatic gain control is necessary to sustain the oscillation at a reasonable level. This control usually has to cover quite a range too, to cope with the mismatches common between the two sections of most ganged pots. Descriptions of this type of circuit often state that the control should act slowly to minimise distortion, especially at low frequencies. They don't usually mention the way in which the rate of operation of the gain control can clash with the rate of the output amplitude's response to it, frequently causing violent instability! Since the Wien Bridge oscillator was invented circuit designers have been struggling to control it, using everything from tungsten lamp filaments and expensive thermistors to LDRs (light dependent resistors) and FETs (field effect transistors) as gain controls.

A field-effect transistor (FET) is relatively simple to use for control so it was chosen for this project. The full circuit of the oscillator is shown in Figure 3.4. The two sections of the bridge use capacitors C1 and C2, with 100k variable resistors and 10k fixed resistors to set the range of just over ten-to-one. For the parallel section, the 10k fixed resistance consists of the four

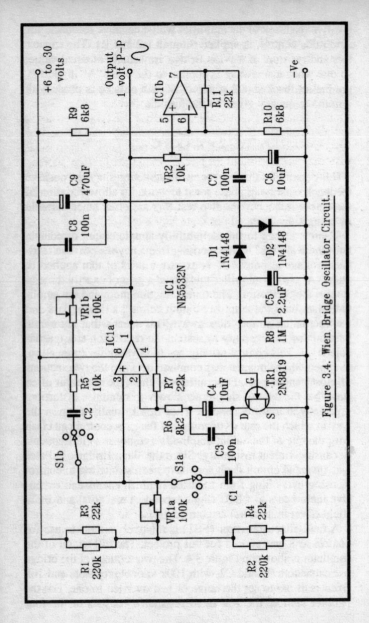

Figure 3.4. Wien Bridge Oscillator Circuit.

64

resistors R1 to R4 which also act as a potential divider to set the DC working point to half the supply voltage, as this circuit is designed to work from a single supply voltage. Their combined resistance is 10k.

Most of the negative feedback is set by resistors R6 and R7, with the FET TR1 used to adjust the precise value. Over a limited range of gate voltage, a junction FET behaves like a variable resistor. The signal voltage across it should be kept low, to about 100mV peak-to-peak, when doing this to avoid distortion. In this circuit R8 initially biases the FET on, increasing the gain of IC1a so that oscillation begins. The oscillator output is amplified by IC1b and rectified by diodes D1 and D2 to produce a negative voltage at the gate of TR1, increasing its resistance to lower the gain of IC1a and reduce its output amplitude. The precise point at which a balance is struck is adjusted with VR2 to suit the particular FET used. If the output is set to about 1 volt peak-to-peak the voltage across the FET will be about 100mV. Once adjusted, the amplitude stays substantially constant right across the frequency range of the circuit and hardly varies at all with changes of supply voltage from six to thirty volts, allowing the circuit to be operated from unregulated battery supplies. Below about 50Hz the amplitude does rise slightly, to a maximum of about 50% over the set level at 10Hz, due to the higher impedance of C7 at low frequency. This range could be omitted for audio work, or the values of C7 and C5 could be adjusted for this range.

The four frequency ranges are set by four pairs of capacitors for C1 and C2, selected with the range switch S1, giving coverage from 10Hz to 100kHz. For clarity only one pair is shown, but the table below shows the values required.

Several dual op-amps were tried in this circuit and most worked well. The best was the 5532, which reached the maximum frequency of 100kHz with ease, but the TLO72 worked almost as well, to 97kHz. The TLO82, LF353, 4558 and 3240 all gave reasonable performance. Devices to avoid are the LM358 and the 1458 as both of these are much too slow. The output amplitude rises slightly below about 40Hz, but is otherwise stable and settles to the working level rapidly following changes of frequency, etc.

The output of 1 volt peak-to-peak is a little low for general

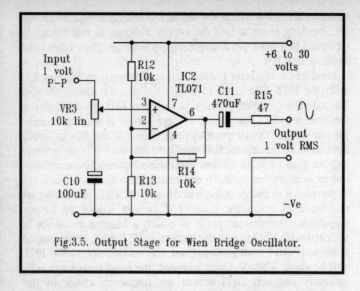

Fig.3.5. Output Stage for Wien Bridge Oscillator.

purpose use, so it can be raised to 1 volt RMS, just below three volts peak-to-peak. Figure 3.5 shows a circuit for this. The "level" control VR3 sets the input to IC2, a TL071 arranged to give a voltage gain of three. The DC blocking capacitor C11 allows the output to be used with the negative supply rail as "ground" whilst resistor R15 gives it an output resistance of just below 50 ohms. This part of the circuit is adjusted by setting the frequency to around 500Hz, turning the output level up to maximum, connecting a test meter to it and adjusting VR3 for 1 volt AC.

Values for C1 and C2:

| Capacitance | Frequency Range |
|---|---|
| 150pF | 10 – 100kHz. |
| 1.5n | 1 – 10kHz |
| 15n | 100Hz – 1kHz |
| 150n | 10 – 100Hz |

These capacitors should be polystyrene or polyester types.

66

*Components for Figures 3.4 and 3.5*

*Resistors* (all 1% metal film, 0.6W)
| | |
|---|---|
| R1, 2 | 220k |
| R3, 4, 7, 11 | 22k (4 off) |
| R5, 12, 13, 14 | 10k (4 off) |
| R6 | 8k2 |
| R8 | 1M |
| R9, 10 | 6k8 (2 off) |
| R15 | 47 ohms |
| VR1 | 100k linear carbon dual-ganged type |
| VR2 | 10k horizontal "cermet" preset. |
| VR3 | 10k linear carbon |

*Capacitors*
| | |
|---|---|
| C1, 2 | see table |
| C3, 7, 8 | 100n resin-dipped ceramic (3 off) |
| C4, 6 | 10µF/50V radial lead electrolytic (2 off) |
| C5 | 2.2µF/100V radial lead electrolytic |
| C9, 11 | 470µF/35V radial lead electrolytic (2 off) |
| C10 | 100µF/35V radial lead electrolytic |

*Semiconductors*
| | |
|---|---|
| D1, 2 | 1N4148 silicon signal diode (2 off) |
| TR1 | 2N3819 N-channel J-FET |
| IC1 | NE5532N dual op-amp |
| IC2 | TL071 op-amp |

*Miscellaneous*
| | |
|---|---|
| S1 | Switch, 2-pole 4-way. |

# Chapter 4

# WAVEFORM GENERATOR IC OSCILLATORS

## The 8038 Function Generator IC

To round off the subject of oscillators using resistors and capacitors to control frequency, a couple of dedicated "function generator" ICs will now be described. The name "function" indicates that they produce more than one output waveform, and they are often referred to as "waveform generators". Sometimes just square and triangle waves are available, but at the time of writing two readily available devices can also produce sinewaves, which can be useful in some designs. Both work in the same way, charging and discharging an external capacitor with constant current and switching the current polarity at preset voltage levels to generate the squarewave and the triangle, and processing the triangle with an internal "shaping" network to obtain the sinewave. From the designer's point of view though, there are some important differences between them.

The earlier device, the 8038, has been around for some years now. It's relatively cheap but a little complicated to use. Maximum frequencies of up 1MHz are claimed for it depending on which manufacturer's data sheet is available. In fact if a reasonably pure output is required it is best not to exceed 100kHz, with an absolute maximum of 200kHz if some distortion at the top end is tolerable. The minimum supply voltage for this device is 10 volts with a maximum of 30 volts, and as it consumes around 20mA it is probably better to forget battery operation and use a mains-powered 20 volt supply.

A general purpose circuit for operating the 8038 is shown in Figure 4.1. A brief description of some of the pin functions should assist experimenters to understand how the IC works. The current flowing into pin 4 controls the rising part of the triangle wave, whilst current flowing into pin 5 controls the falling part. Varying the ratio of these two therefore varies the duty cycle and can be used to produce sawtooth and pulse waveforms, although this is outside the scope of this chapter. For a reasonably pure sinewave some duty-cycle minor

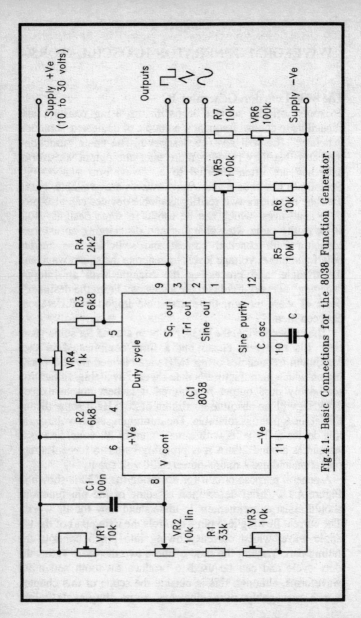

Fig.4.1. Basic Connections for the 8038 Function Generator.

adjustment is usually necessary, this being given by the preset VR4. Also for optimum sinewave purity two further preset adjustments can be made to pins 1 and 12 by VR5 and VR6. This calls for a method of indicating the output distortion though, so if this is not available or maximum possible purity is not required, they can be omitted with pin 1 left unconnected and pin 12 connected to negative rail through an 82k resistor.

All three outputs are available simultaneously. The triangle is provided from pin 3, the sinewave from pin 2 and the squarewave from pin 9. The squarewave output is sourced from the collector of an internal transistor which can sink current to ground but not supply it so the "pull-up" resistor R4 is required. There is an inevitable conflict between power consumption and speed here. The falling edge of the squarewave is fast as it is actively pulled down by the transistor, but the rise time will be slower since it is set by the time constant of the resistor combined with stray and transistor collector capacitance. The lower the resistor the faster the rise time, but the heavier the current whilst the transistor is on. Note that the resistor doesn't have to be returned to the main positive supply. It could, for instance, be connected to a separate 5-volt logic supply to generate a TTL-compatible output. The amplitude levels of the three outputs differ, the squarewave being practically supply voltage peak-to-peak, the triangle about a third of this and the sinewave about a fifth. The average DC value of all the outputs is always exactly half the supply, so if a split supply is used they will be symmetrical about "ground".

In addition to the resistors connected to pins 4 and 5, the frequency is set by the capacitor between pin 10 and ground and it can be varied by a voltage applied to pin 8. The capacitor is usually chosen to set the range using values from 100pF up to 100µF or more. Electrolytics can be used, though the wide tolerance of their values means individual selection will probably be necessary. The table shows values of "C" which can be used with the circuit shown to build the "front-end" of an inexpensive 2Hz to 200kHz general purpose function generator. The control voltage from VR2 sweeps the output across the selected range, and with the values shown it can be set up to give a 10–1 ratio. Note that the action of VR2 is inverted as the lower the control voltage, the higher the output frequency.

Values of "C" for various frequency ranges:

| Capacitance | Frequency |
|---|---|
| 200pF | 20 to 200kHz |
| 2.2n | 2 to 20kHz |
| 22n | 200Hz to 2kHz |
| 220n | 20 to 200Hz |
| 2.2µF | 2 to 20Hz |

Capacitors should be polystyrene or polyester types.

*Components for Figure 4.1*

*Resistors* (all 1% metal film, 0.6W)

| R1 | 33k |
|---|---|
| R2, 3 | 6k8 (2 off) |
| R4 | 2k2 |
| R5 | 10M |
| R6, 7 | 10k (2 off) |
| VR1, 3 | 10k preset (2 off) |
| VR2 | 10k linear carbon pot |
| VR4 | 1k preset |
| VR5, 6 | 100k preset (2 off) |

*Semiconductors*

| IC1 | 8038 waveform generator. |
|---|---|

## The MAX038 Function Generator

The second "function generator" device to be described is a relative newcomer to the market, in fact it was released during the preparation of this book. This is the Maxim MAX038, which is probably destined to replace the older device as the industry standard waveform generator. Whilst it also provides triangle, square and sinewave outputs, there are many differences which designers and experimenters should know about. In some ways it is a lot easier to use than its predecessor, but in others it can prove more difficult. The single most important

72

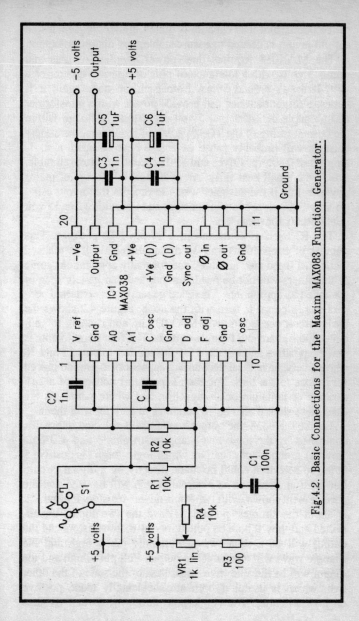

Fig.4.2. Basic Connections for the Maxim MAX083 Function Generator.

73

difference is that it is capable of much higher frequencies so careful layout is needed to ensure stable, low distortion output.

The MAX038 requires dual power supplies of plus and minus 5 volts with a tolerance of plus or minus a quarter of a volt. It draws around 50mA from each, so once again it is better to forget batteries and provide power with a transformer and a couple of 3-terminal 5-volt regulators. Although within the current rating of the TO92 packaged regulators, the supply currents will probably cause excessive heat dissipation so 1-amp types 7805 (positive) and 7905 (negative) are preferable, fitted with small heat sinks. An additional advantage of mains power is that if the designer wants to process the output using op-amps, the supply can be constructed to provide 12 or 15 volt dual outputs for these too.

The IC itself is contained in a 20-pin DIL package. This number of connections may seem daunting until it is realised that six of these are "ground", and for many applications some of the others will not be needed either and can be left open or grounded as appropriate. There are generally less external connections to be made than with the 8038. Figure 4.2 shows the basic circuit needed to get a MAX038 up and running to generate sine, square and triangle outputs. The first point to note is that the positive and negative 5-volt supplies, to pins 17 and 20 respectively, have local decoupling capacitors to ground placed very close to the pins. For each supply this consists of a 1µF ceramic or tantalum bead capacitor, and where tantalums are used there should also be 1n ceramics in parallel with them.

Unlike the 8038, the output waveform is selected internally, controlled by the logic levels applied to pins 3 and 4. Logic "low" is ground, not negative, whilst logic "high" is positive 5 volts, so selection could be made directly by a digital circuit. For most applications an external switch will be used and the arrangement shown, with two "pull-down" resistors R1 and R2, is about the simplest possible. Leave the two inputs unconnected and they'll both be pulled low by these resistors and the output will be a squarewave. Pull only pin 4 high and the triangle wave will appear at the output. Pull pin 3 high and the output will be the sinewave, regardless of the state of the other two, which is useful if both are accidentally made positive during switching. The single-pole three-way switch S1 thus determines the waveform, and because no high frequency signals pass through it, wiring layout to it is non-critical. The output, from pin 19, has a constant amplitude of 2 volts peak to peak for all three waveforms and a very low output impedance which simplifies the design of following circuitry considerably in comparison with the 8038.

The frequency is controlled by the value of the capacitor "C" between pin 5 and ground and the current flowing into pin 10. The capacitor can have any value between about 20pF and 100μF or more. It should be placed so that the ground connection is close to pin 6. A small trimmer can be used together with a fixed capacitor to compensate for stray capacitance for high frequency ranges. Although never really a good choice for timing and frequency generation circuits, an electrolytic can be used, with the positive end towards pin 5, as the IC charges and discharges it between zero (ground) and one volt positive.

The output frequency is linearly proportional to the current flowing into pin 10, for values between 2μA and 750μA. Since pin 10 is always at ground potential, all that is needed to provide a linear controlled current is a variable voltage and a resistor. For many applications the arrangement shown in Figure 4.2, with VR1 and R3 setting a ten-to-one voltage range and R4 to convert it to a current, will be all that is needed. The frequency is given theoretically by:

$$\frac{\text{Input current I}}{\text{Capacitance C}}$$

which is much simpler than many of the other circuits in this book. The output actually produced conforms closely to this formula for most values of I and C. The IC is normally specified as capable of operating up to 20MHz. At this frequency there is some apparent distortion, but at 10MHz the sine and triangle waveforms are excellent and even the squarewave is still recognisably rectangular.

Now for a few cautions and "don't"s. Pin 1 is a reference voltage output of 2.55 volts from an internal "bandgap" source, intended for use in generating input currents. The data sheet says it can supply up to 4mA, but neither of two examples tested by the author managed more than 1mA. Greater loading than this caused a drop in the reference voltage. This is much worse news than at first appears because this reference is also used by internal circuits of the chip. If it is pulled down the frequency rises, the output amplitude dips, and heavy distortion occurs in sine and triangle outputs. It is probably better to provide this pin with a 1n ceramic decoupling capacitor as shown and otherwise leave it alone. It could be buffered with an op-amp, but since a regulated 5-volt positive supply should already be available at much higher current, why bother?

The next point to watch out for is the action of an internal comparator, with a 5 volt output available from pin 14 which can be used to provide a logic-level synchronising signal. The output of this has very fast rise and fall times and unless great care is taken with layout, using a double-sided "ground-plane" PCB, it has a tendency to find its way through stray capacitive coupling to the main output, causing distortion and spikes. It has a separate positive power supply at pin 16, so if it is not needed this can be left unconnected to disable it. However the "digital ground" at pin 15 should be connected to ground, otherwise the comparator's input circuit will still cause severe distortion.

Figure 4.2 shows all that is required to get this IC working to generate clean 2-volt peak-to-peak outputs all the way up to 10MHz and beyond. There are other features available of which designers should be aware, although a full description is beyond the scope of this book. Pin 7 is a "duty cycle adjust" input which, if supplied with a voltage between plus and minus 2.3 volts will alter the duty cycle from 15% to 85% whilst having practically no effect on the frequency. This can be used to generate sawtooth or pulse waveforms. Connecting it to ground as shown results in a 50–50 duty cycle. Pin 8 is a "frequency adjust", which, when fed with a similar control voltage, will vary the output frequency between 0.3 and 1.7 times its nominal value. The obvious applications for this are frequency sweeping or a "fine tune" control. This too can be grounded if not required. Both these inputs have internal 250μA current sinks to the negative supply so they should never be left unconnected. If they are supplied through resistors, the effect of these currents must be allowed for. Finally, there is an on-board phase comparator which can be used for synchronising the output frequency to another signal. This has an input to pin 13, and an output from pin 12. With suitable filtering it can supply a voltage to pin 8, the "frequency adjust" input, for true phase-locked loop operation.

Provided the layout considerations are kept in mind, this is actually a much easier device to use than the 8038. There are less preset adjustments to be made, control is simpler and more accurate and the performance is superior in just about every way. The sinewave output in particular is very good, even at high frequency, much better than it's predecessor. The price is a small snag at the time of writing, but at around £15.00 it is not really prohibitive and in time will probably fall considerably.

Values of "C" for various frequency ranges:

| Capacitor | Frequency range |
|-----------|-----------------|
| 22pF | 1 to 10MHz |
| 220pF | 100kHz to 1MHz |
| 2.2n | 10 to 100kHz |
| 22n | 1 to 10kHz |
| 220n | 100Hz to 1kHz |
| 2.2µF | 10 to 100Hz |

Capacitors should be polystyrene or polyester types. A trimmer can be used for the highest range.

*Components for Figure 4.2*

*Resistors* (all 1% metal film, 0.6W)
R1, 2, 4          10k (3 off)
R3                100ohm
VR1               1k linear carbon pot

*Capacitors*
C1                100n ceramic
C2, 3, 4          1n ceramic
C5, 6             1µF/35V tantalum bead

*Semiconductors*
IC1               MAX038 waveform generator. (Maxim).

# Chapter 5

# INDUCTOR CAPACITOR OSCILLATORS

## LC Oscillator Circuits

In this chapter circuits are given for some oscillators using resonant coil and capacitor combinations to determine frequency. Whilst this type tends to be restricted to circuits operating at radio frequencies, there is no reason why this should always be so. Many component suppliers now offer useful ranges of small inductors, either as tiny potted ferrite devices or wire-ended "chokes" which are very similar in appearance to resistors and using these, it is possible to generate frequencies down into the audio range. The output frequency is generally far more stable than that of the CR circuits describes so far, especially at high frequencies, and may provide a useful alternative to crystals in many frequency-generating circuits. Though not as easy to tune as CR circuits, they are much better than crystals in this respect. For experimenting, the inductors are cheaper than crystals and can be tuned to a wide range of frequencies by selection of the capacitors used with them. Whilst low frequencies could use large inductors and capacitors, a useful alternative technique is to reduce the high frequency of an LC oscillator with a CMOS divider, resulting in a very stable low frequency. The entire process can frequently be done by a single inexpensive IC.

Many designers find a mental picture of the circuit action is a help when designing, both in figuring out what is happening if it fails to perform as expected and in creating fresh versions of it. One way of doing this is to use the "water analogy", where the flow of current is compared to the flow of water along a pipe with the voltage being seen as the pressure driving it. Using this comparison, an inductor can be thought of as a mass of water flowing in a long pipe, its inertia causing it to take up (or release) energy with any change in speed. A capacitor in such a system would consist of a wide section of pipe with a rubber diaphragm placed across it, which would prevent a steady flow (DC) but would allow an oscillating movement (AC), the amount depending on the pressure and stiffness of the diaphragm.

If the ends of these two hypothetical devices are connected together the result will be the equivalent of a parallel LC "tank" circuit. If the water in the pipe is given an initial push it will bounce back and forth as its inertia reacts with the springiness of the diaphragm. This is similar to current in the electrical circuit. Friction in the pipe will cause the oscillations to die away and eventually stop, again a useful comparison as oscillations in the electrical circuit usually lose power mainly because of resistance in the coil. If a way is found to sense the water movement and give it a suitably timed nudge during each cycle the system becomes an oscillator, just like the electrical version.

All too often LC oscillator circuits give disappointing results when constructed. They may distort, burst into unwanted parasitic frequencies, or simply fail to work at all. This is often caused by coil characteristics, which are not as easy to determine as those of resistors and capacitors. Coils may be anything from high-Q inductors on ferrite pot cores, through home-wound items on bits of ferrite rod to air-cored types with very few turns. Circuits with high operating frequencies often use a single transistor or FET for sustaining the oscillation in place of the op-amps and CMOS gates found elsewhere in this book. The component values used in such circuits often need "tweaking" to obtain optimum performance, requiring suitable test equipment to examine the results. The aim in this chapter is to provide a number of circuits, using both discrete devices and CMOS gates, that have proved to be fairly reliable with various frequencies and coil types. Most of the transistor and FET types are capable of low distortion, though an oscilloscope may be needed for adjusting this. The CMOS types by their nature contain squarewaves somewhere in the circuit, but they are simple, very reliable, and the waveform across the LC tank circuit is often fairly "clean".

## Coil and Capacitor Values
All the circuits of this chapter use "parallel-resonant" tuned circuits to fix the operating frequency. At resonance, the reactances (AC impedances) of the inductance and the capacitance are identical (although opposite in sign). For any resonant frequency there is a large number of inductor and capacitor

80

combinations that could be used so one problem is to decide which of the many possible values will be most suitable.

In the water-based equivalent, the main source of loss was friction in the pipe. This suggests that the less actual movement takes place, the less the friction losses will be. This points to use of a lot of water and a stiff diaphragm so that most of the energy movement will be in the form of pressure change instead of motion. The electrical equivalent is, within reasonable limits, a large inductance and a small capacitance. How large, and how small? Guidance on this point is hard to find, but in general the author has found that selecting values of L and C to have impedances of about 1000 ohms at the operating frequency will usually give reasonable results. This is a very rough guide and use of components having several times this value, or a small fraction of it, will often have little effect on oscillator performance. However, it does at least provide a starting point for design.

The formulae for LC oscillator calculations are quite simple.

The reactance of a capacitor is given by:

$$\frac{1}{2 \times \pi \times f \times C}$$

Where $f$ is the frequency in hertz of the applied voltage and C is capacitance in farads.

The reactance of an inductance is given by:

$$2 \times \pi \times f \times L$$

where $f$ is again the frequency, and L is the inductance in henries.

Normally the values of C will be in picofarads (pF) or nanofarads (nF), and the inductance in millihenries (mH) or microhenries (μH). Many calculators allow direct entry of the necessary "powers-of-ten" for such calculations.

At resonance the results of the two above formulae are equal for the components in use. Some rearrangement therefore shows that at resonance, the frequency is given by:

$$f = \frac{1}{2 \times \pi \times \sqrt{L \times C}}$$

The units again being hertz, henries and farads. With a little practice these calculations become very easy to perform.

For some applications constructors might like to construct their own coils. This is a bit of a trial-and-error procedure as various types of ferrite have different characteristics, but as a very rough guide 50 turns of 0.4mm enamelled copper wire on a length of 9mm diameter ferrite rod should have an inductance of about 250µH. A point to note is that the inductance is proportional to the square of the number of turns. Therefore, if a value of 500µH is needed, the turns should not be increased to 100 turns, instead the figure would be:

$$\sqrt{\frac{500}{250}} \times 50 = 70.71$$

so somewhere around 70 turns is needed. This applies to most coil types, though inductance also varies with length along the axis, permeability of the core material, diameter of the wire and so on. Coil winding is an area where there is no substitute for practical experiment.

**Transistor Hartley Oscillator**
All oscillator circuits need positive feedback in order to sustain oscillation. To suit the amplifying device used, the feedback signal may need a change in level or impedance and, as in the case of a transistor circuit where it is taken from the collector and applied at the base, it may need polarity inversion. This is often achieved by using a "tap" in the tuned circuit. Some of the basic LC oscillator circuits are named after the engineers who originally thought of them, and the main difference between these is often the way in which the tank circuit is tapped. With the Hartley circuit, the coil is tapped. This is easy enough to provide in the case of home-wound coils, making this a useful circuit for use when experimenting with RF signals.

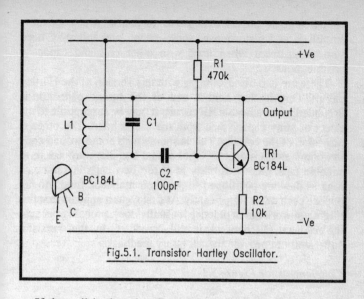

Fig.5.1. Transistor Hartley Oscillator.

If the coil is thought of as a simple transformer, it will be seen that if the tap is grounded, then a positive polarity excursion applied to one end will result in a negative one at the other, and vice-versa. The tap can provide a voltage or impedance change if there is a difference in the number of turns to each side of it, though in many simple circuits it is sufficient to use a centre-tap. In the circuit of Figure 5.1 the collector current of transistor TR1 flows through one half of the coil to the positive supply rail, and the positive feedback taken from the other is applied to the base through DC blocking capacitor C2. Capacitor C1 combines with coil L1 to set the resonant frequency, and can be a variable type as used for tuning AM radios. The version tested used 60 turns of 0.4mm enamelled copper wire close-wound on a 9mm diameter ferrite rod and when tuned with a 5–240pF variable capacitor for C1 covered a range of 0.6 to 1.6MHz with a reasonably pure output waveform. This is approximately the AM radio medium wave range, so the circuit can be used for testing such radios.

The Hartley is a lively oscillator which easily produces high signal voltage levels but is prone to distortion though overdriving of the resonant circuit. The resistor R2 in the

83

emitter circuit provides negative feedback which controls amplitude and distortion to some extent, and this may need some adjustment when used with other coil and capacitor combinations.

There are two disadvantages with this version of the Hartley circuit. One is that neither end of the tuning capacitor is grounded, so in tuneable RF circuits it may be susceptible to the effect of stray capacitance from the user's hand. The other is provision of the coil tap. This is simple with home-wound coils but commercial inductors, chokes and the like may not have suitable taps. One possibility is to use two coils in series, so long as they are positioned so that their magnetic fields do not oppose each other significantly. At first sight it appears that this might not work but in practice it usually does, probably because the resonant CR network is still "prodded" by the transistor sufficiently to provide the necessary feedback.

*Components for Figure 5.1*

*Resistors* (all metal film, 0.6W)
R1          470k
R2          10k (but see text)

*Capacitors*
C1          see text
C2          100pF polystyrene
            (could be increased for lower frequencies)

*Coil*
L1          see text

*Semiconductor*
TR1         BC184L (although most small silicon NPN
            transistors should work in this circuit)

## Transistor Colpitts Oscillator

To avoid the need for a tapped coil, it is possible to tap the capacitor of the resonant circuit instead. Although it may not be immediately apparent, this in fact has exactly the same effect as a tap on the coil and can be used in the same way. Like the

84

Hartley this type of circuit is named after its inventor, an engineer by the name of Colpitts. Apart from removing the need for a tapped coil, the Colpitts oscillator is less lively than the Hartley and so can more easily be used for generating a signal of reasonable purity, so it is often found in RF signal generators.

There are now two tuning capacitors however, and since they are in series their effective capacitance is reduced. For tuneable versions of the Colpitts, variable capacitors having two equal sides can be obtained. At one time large and solidly-constructed air-spaced tuning capacitors were commonplace and many constructors may still have at least one of these, possibly salvaged from the stripping of an old radio. New ones can still be purchased from some suppliers, though their price tends to be a trifle prohibitive. However, there is no reason why one of the small and cheap plastic-cased types should not be used instead. The tap between the capacitors is connected to ground, thereby eliminating the stray capacitance problem of the previous circuit.

A single-transistor version of the Colpitts circuit is shown in Figure 5.2. For fixed frequency operation, wire-ended chokes or tiny inductors can be used in this circuit together with fixed capacitors. It would then also be possible to vary the ratio of the capacitor values to experiment with impedance matching, possibly increasing C2 with respect to C1 to reduce the drive input to the base of TR1. As in the previous circuit, the emitter resistor R3 controls the amplitude and purity of the output. For some combinations of L and C it may be necessary to use a capacitor to bypass all or part of this resistor, and the amount could be made adjustable by using a preset resistor to obtain optimum results. The inset next to R3 shows how this can be done. When calculating the operating frequency of this circuit, remember that the value of "C" is now that of C1 and C2 in series, which is given by:

$$C = \cfrac{1}{\cfrac{1}{C1} + \cfrac{1}{C2}}$$

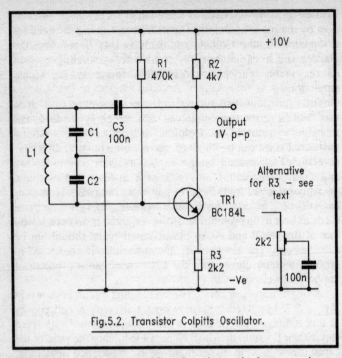

Fig.5.2. Transistor Colpitts Oscillator.

where C1 and C2 are equal in value, the equivalent capacitance is half the value of one of them.

*Components for Figure 5.2*

*Resistors* (all metal film, 0.6W)
| | |
|---|---|
| R1 | 470k |
| R2 | 4k7 |
| R3 | 2k2 |

*Capacitors*
| | |
|---|---|
| C1, 2 | see text |
| C3 | 100n polyester |

*Coil*
| | |
|---|---|
| L1 | see text |

*Semiconductor*
| | |
|---|---|
| TR1 | BC184L NPN silicon |

## Transistor Colpitts, Emitter Feedback

The version of the Colpitts oscillator shown in Figure 5.2 took its feedback from the collector of the transistor. To turn this into positive feedback phase inversion was needed, but only a small signal voltage as the transistor provides plenty of voltage amplification at its collector. Another version of the Colpitts circuit, Figure 5.3, often found in signal generators, obtains its feedback from the emitter. Because of the absence of voltage gain at this point this version of the circuit can often be designed to give a more pure and stable signal. The phase inversion is no longer needed with feedback from this point, but as the emitter signal voltage is always very slightly smaller than the signal applied to the base some voltage increase in the feedback is required if the oscillator is to work. Capacitors C1 and C2 again form the tap which is driven by the signal taken from the emitter of the transistor TR1. The voltage at the top of C1 is higher than the drive signal, by a factor of about two if the capacitors are of equal value, but is in phase with it for connection through C3 to the transistor base.

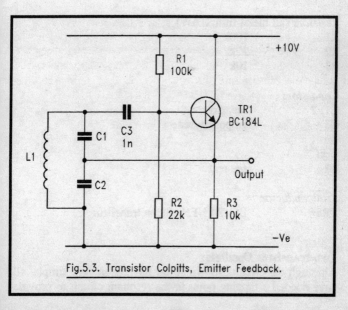

Fig.5.3. Transistor Colpitts, Emitter Feedback.

As with the previous Colpitts circuit the capacitors C1 and C2 may be a dual variable type, but this time their common point is not grounded, which may cause stray capacitance problems depending on the physical arrangement of the circuit. One possibility is to use a fixed capacitor for C1 and a smaller, single-gang variable component for C2. There will be some variation in output amplitude across the frequency range if this is done though, and the coverage will be smaller. However it may be a useful option for circuits that need only a small adjustment range, perhaps for trimming purposes.

The gain of this circuit may need trimming to obtain a reasonably pure output waveform. Adjustment of the value of R3 will normally allow very good results to be achieved.

Although not shown, the Hartley circuit can also use feedback from the transistor emitter, with drive to the coil tap and a single tuning capacitor. Like its collector feedback equivalent it tends to be livelier and may need more negative feedback to obtain a low-distortion output signal.

*Components for Figure 5.3*

*Resistors* (all metal film, 0.6W)
| | |
|---|---|
| R1 | 100k |
| R2 | 22k |
| R3 | 10k |

*Capacitors*
| | |
|---|---|
| C1, 2 | see text |
| C3 | 1n polystyrene |

*Coil*
| | |
|---|---|
| L1 | see text |

*Semiconductor*
| | |
|---|---|
| TR1 | BC184 NPN silicon transistor |

**Two-transistor Oscillator**
Although the circuits shown so far have been very simple, all have needed a tapping point in the resonant circuit to provide

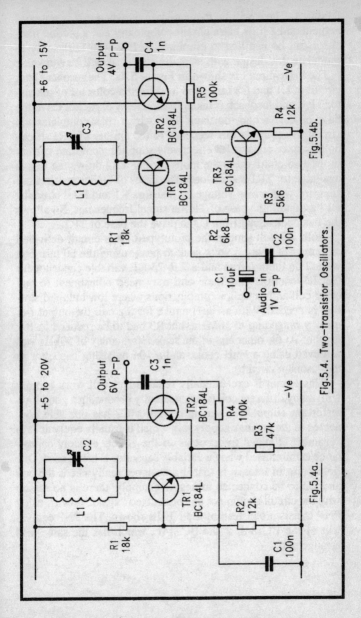

Fig.5.4. Two-transistor Oscillators.

**Fig.5.4b.**

Output 4V p-p
+6 to 15V
C4 1n
TR2 BC184L
R5 100k
TR1 BC184L
L1
C3
TR3 BC184L
R4 12k
R1 18k
R2 6k8
R3 5k6
C2 100n
C1 10uF
Audio in 1V p-p
−Ve

**Fig.5.4a.**

+5 to 20V
Output 6V p-p
C3 1n
TR2 BC184L
R4 100k
L1
C2
TR1 BC184L
R3 47k
R1 18k
R2 12k
C1 100n
−Ve

feedback. There will be many occasions when this is not convenient and a little extra circuit complexity and a second transistor can be justified to eliminate it. It is also fairly easy to modulate this design with an audio signal, as will be shown.

The basic circuit is shown in Figure 5.4a. The resonant tank circuit of L1 and C2 forms the load for the collector of transistor TR1, and feedback is taken from here by capacitor C3 to the base of the second transistor TR2 which then completes the circuit by returning this feedback to the emitter of TR1. It can do this since resistor R3 effectively supplies a constant current to the two emitters, so the more current TR2 draws the less is available for TR1 and its load. The bases of both transistors are supplied with a bias voltage by resistors R1 and R2, but whilst C1 "grounds" the base of TR1 at signal frequencies, R4 allows the feedback signal from C3 to drive the base of TR2.

With a 9-volt supply, the prototype of this circuit delivered an output of about 6 volts peak to peak, using the 60 turn coil wound on 9mm ferrite and a 5 to 250pF variable capacitor for C2. R3 controls amplitude and may need adjustment to suit other coil and capacitor combinations where low output distortion is needed. With a 10µH choke for the coil the output frequency ranged up to 10MHz, but R3 had to be reduced to 10k for this. At the other end of the scale a frequency of 50kHz was achieved using a 1mH choke and a 10n polyester capacitor as the resonant circuit.

This circuit is exceptionally reliable and will work happily with many different coil types, generally producing a good low-distortion output. The tuning capacitor C2 has one side connected to the positive supply rail, which is usually equivalent to "ground" at signal frequencies so the effects of stray capacitance is minimised when a variable capacitor is being used. One final point of interest is that if a designer really needs the coil and C2 to be connected to negative supply, there is no reason why the circuit should not be constructed "upside down", using PNP transistors instead of the NPN's shown. The PNP equivalent of the BC184L is the BC214L, which has the same lead arrangement.

*Components for Figure 5.4a*

**Resistors** (all metal film, 0.6W)
R1             18k
R2             12k
R3             47k (see text)

**Capacitors**
C1             100n polyester
C2             see text
C3             1n polystyrene

**Coil**
L1             see text

**Semiconductors**
TR1, 2         BC184L NPN silicon transistor (2 off)

Audio modulation can be applied to this circuit quite easily. Since the emitter resistor controls the output amplitude, it can be replaced with a transistor current source as shown in Figure 5.4b and this can be used for modulating the signal. The bias chain has an additional resistor, R3, to provide bias for this transistor. Current drawn through the emitter resistor R4 is delivered from the collector to the emitters of TR1 and TR2. This current is dependent upon the base voltage, so it can be modulated by applying an audio signal through C1. With a 9 volt power supply the level of the modulation signal should be about 1 volt peak-to-peak, though this may vary with different combinations of L1 and C3, and with different supply voltages. The average output amplitude level can also be adjusted by altering the value of emitter resistor R4.

As with most simple modulation systems the output from this circuit is a mixture of amplitude and frequency modulation, but it can be used to couple a signal into a nearby AM radio with quite acceptable results for testing or perhaps using the radio as a simple audio amplifier.

*Components for Figure 5.4b*

*Resistors* (all metal film, 0.6W)
| | |
|---|---|
| R1 | 18k |
| R2 | 6k8 |
| R3 | 5k6 |
| R4 | 12k |
| R5 | 100k |

*Capacitors*
| | |
|---|---|
| C1 | 10µF/25V electrolytic |
| C2 | 100n polyester |
| C3 | see text |
| C4 | 1n polystyrene |

*Coil*
| | |
|---|---|
| L1 | see text |

*Semiconductors*
| | |
|---|---|
| TR1, 2, 3 | BC184L NPN silicon transistor (3 off) |

## Complementary Two-transistor Oscillator

This interesting two-transistor circuit, shown in Figure 5.5, is similar to the one of Figure 5.4a, but this time uses transistors of complementary polarity, one NPN and one PNP. Again it is very simple and reliable, though performance is not so good when operated at higher frequencies. The version tested was found to distort a bit above 1MHz. However, it is a very good low-frequency circuit and retains the advantage of not requiring a tap in the coil or capacitor. A 1mH choke with a 100n polyester capacitor worked well, giving a frequency of just 15kHz, and there is no reason why the circuit should not work at even lower frequencies than this. A very wide range of supply voltages can be used, the test version worked quite happily with supplies from 3 to 30 volts!

The resonant LC circuit L1 and C2 forms the collector load for the PNP transistor TR1 which, like TR1 of the previous circuit, has its base grounded at signal frequency by capacitor C1. Feedback and bias current is provided to the base of the

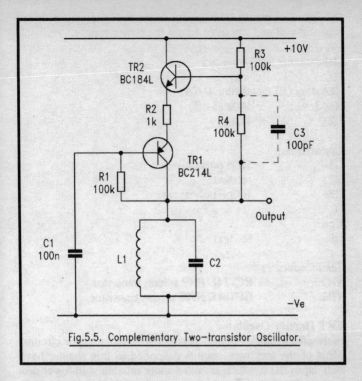

Fig.5.5. Complementary Two-transistor Oscillator.

NPN transistor TR2 by R3, this then controls TR1 emitter current through R2

Output amplitude can be adjusted by altering the value of R2. For maximum amplitude the feedback can be increased by the addition of C3 across R4, though practical tests will be needed to see if this is suitable with the coil being used. With a coil of reasonable "Q" and a low operating frequency, experiments showed that both R2 and C3 can be omitted altogether resulting in a very simple and economical circuit with a very good waveform, though this is not recommended with a poor "Q" or high frequency.

Like the last circuit, this one can be built the "other way up", returning the coil and C2 connections to the positive rail instead of the negative, by simply swapping the transistors. In many circuits C1 could be returned to either rail, making possible a

93

two-terminal circuit that can be connected in series with the resonant coil and capacitor across the power supply.

*Components for Figure 5.5*

*Resistors* (all metal film, 0.6W)
R1, 3, 4          100k (3 off)
R2                1k

*Capacitors*
C1                100n polyester
C2                see text
C3                100pF polystyrene

*Coil*
L1                see text

*Semiconductors*
TR1               BC214L PNP silicon transistor
TR2               BC184L NPN silicon transistor

**FET Hartley Oscillator**
Field effect transistors also perform well in oscillator circuits. Most of the transistor circuits described in this chapter have FET equivalents which are often more reliable with lower distortion. Biasing arrangements are often simpler too, and in many cases a strategically placed diode will control the gate voltage, giving automatic amplitude level control to make the output level substantially independent of supply voltage changes.

Figure 5.6 shows a basic Hartley circuit with the coil driven from the drain of the FET. The feedback is applied through capacitor C2 to the gate whilst resistor R2 in series with the supply to the source sets up the correct DC conditions and controls the signal amplitude. Like most N-channel field effect transistors the gate of the 2N3819 has to be biased so that it is negative with respect to the source, so if the gate is grounded and the source is provided with a series resistor the source voltage will rise until a balance is struck where the increasingly negative gate voltage prevents further increase in source

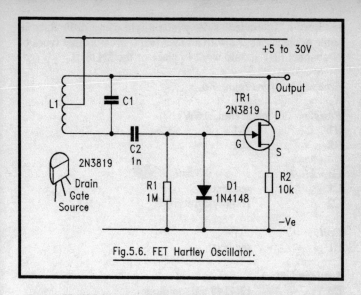

Fig.5.6. FET Hartley Oscillator.

current. Unlike bipolar resistors, this voltage varies quite a bit between individual FETs and circuit designs should take this variation into account. However, the arrangement shown will always bias the FET into its linear active region, allowing oscillation to start. For a given supply voltage the value of R2 could be simply adjusted for the output level required as FET circuits tend to be self-stabilising to some extent anyway. However, the addition of the diode D1 improves stabilisation further by generating a negative charge on the gate side of C2 as the amplitude of the feedback rises, and the level then remains more or less constant over a wide range of supply voltage.

The circuit shown actually ran with a supply of just 2 volts, though a minimum of 5 volts is recommended. As the supply voltage was increased the output level stabilised at about 10 volts peak-to-peak and remained constant right up to 30 volts input. With source resistors of 10k and higher the output waveform purity was excellent.

This circuit operates well up to and beyond 10MHz. The coil does require a tap of course, tests were carried out with the 60-turn home-wound coil on ferrite with a centre tap. The tuning capacitor C1 was a 5–250pF variable type. In this circuit it does not have a "grounded" side, which might cause difficulties in some applications. As with all these FET circuits other types of N-channel FET should work in place of the 2N3819.

*Components for Figure 5.6*

*Resistors* (all metal film, 0.6W)
R1          1M
R2          10k

*Capacitors*
C1          see text
C2          1n polystyrene

*Coil*
L1          see text

*Semiconductors*
D1          1N4148 silicon diode
TR1         2N3819 N-channel FET.


## FET Hartley Oscillator, Source Feedback

Drive for the resonant LC circuit can be taken from the source of the FET instead of the drain, as shown in Figure 5.7. This usually results in lower signal amplitude across the coil, but the output waveform can be better. It also has the advantage that one end of the tuning capacitor C1 and coil L1 is connected to ground, which can be used to minimise the effects of stray capacitance where a variable capacitor is to be used. Like the bipolar transistor version the feedback from the source does not need phase inversion, but it does need a small increase in voltage which is achieved by driving the coil through its tap with the source. The DC path for the source is through the coil, so the source resistor has been omitted and instead, the negative gate bias is generated by the diode D1. This increases as the amplitude of the oscillation builds up until a balance is reached, so the circuit has automatic level control.

With just three components in addition to the FET and the tank circuit L1 and C1, this circuit produces an excellent output

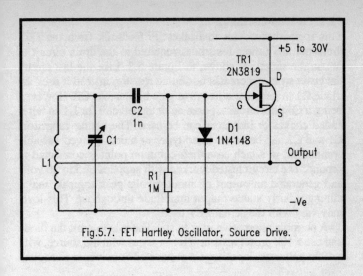

Fig.5.7. FET Hartley Oscillator, Source Drive.

waveform. The amplitude from the one tested settled at about 4 volts peak-to-peak and remained substantially constant with supply voltages from 3 to 30 volts, though this may vary with the characteristics of the FET used.. The supply current was just 50µA. It should work with a wide variety of coil and capacitor types, the prototype was tested with the 60-turn ferrite rod coil and 5–250pF tuning capacitor.

*Components for Figure 5.7*

*Resistor* (all metal film, 0.6W)
R1                1M

*Capacitors*
C1                see text
C2                1n polystyrene

*Coil*
L1                see text

*Semiconductors*
D1                1N4148 silicon signal diode
TR1               2N3819 N-channel FET

## FET Colpitts Oscillator

This is another circuit that takes its feedback from the FET drain but this time a resistor is required in the drain circuit to obtain the signal, as shown in Figure 5.8. Like the last circuit the basic arrangement has no source resistor, instead it uses the diode D1 to generate a negative gate bias across C2. However, being a Colpitts circuit, it uses an untapped coil for L1 so wire-ended chokes or inductors can be used. The tuning capacitors C1 and C2 can be either fixed types or a dual-ganged variable component, in which case their common point is connected to ground. The circuit tested worked with supplies of 5 to 30 volts and generated an output of about 4 volts peak-to-peak, maintaining a fairly stable output amplitude throughout. This level may vary with the actual FET used.

A possible alternative way to stabilise it is to omit the diode and use a 10k preset resistor VR1 in series with the source, with a 100n polyester capacitor C4 connected to its wiper as shown.

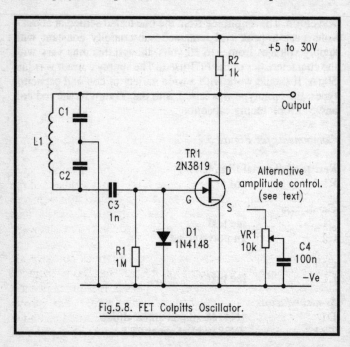

Fig.5.8. FET Colpitts Oscillator.

This can then be used to adjust the output level to some predetermined level with different FETs and coils. When set to 1 volt peak-to-peak, the output was found to be very pure and the amplitude remained constant right across the full supply voltage range. Frequencies of 10MHz and more were generated easily with this circuit.

*Components for Figure 5.8*

*Resistors* (all metal film, 0.6W)
R1          1M
R2          1k
VR1         10k (if used)

*Capacitors*
C1, 2       see text
C3          1n polystyrene
C4          100n polyester

*Coil*
L1          see text

*Semiconductors*
D1          1N4148 silicon signal diode
TR1         2N3819 N-channel FET

## FET Colpitts Oscillator, Source Feedback

Two more versions of the Colpitts circuit are shown in Figure 5.9, this time driving the resonant circuit from the source of the FET. This circuit is often seen in RF signal generators, amateur HF transmitters and the like. When correctly designed, it is capable of providing a very pure, harmonic-free sinewave signal.

The first version, shown in Figure 5.9a, does not have the very best output waveform purity but has been included because it is so simple. Just a single resistor is required in addition to the resonant LC components and the FET. The version tested for this chapter, using a 2N3819 with assorted combinations of coils and capacitors, produced a peak-to-peak signal of almost twice the supply voltage across the coil. The waveform across the coil and capacitors was actually quite good, but if the signal is taken from the source it will probably contain some distortion due to the high drive level applied to the FET gate. However, for a healthy output level and maximum simplicity, this circuit is hard to beat. Increasing the value of R1 to 100k improves the signal waveform but reduces the amplitude to about 2 volts peak-to-peak, and for most uses it would probably require a buffer of some kind. This circuit can be operated from a wide range of supply voltages, from 5 to at least 30 volts.

An improved version is shown in Figure 5.9b. Here the feedback path to the gate of the FET has a DC blocking capacitor C3, which allows the diode D1 to generate a negative gate bias voltage in a similar manner to that of some of the circuits described earlier. This controls the amplitude of oscillation, resulting in a cleaner output signal from the FET source and a very stable output level, which may initially be set by selection of a suitable value for the source resistor. Tests showed that to avoid distortion the value of this resistor should be at least 10k, but the circuit still worked with a 100k resistor here, giving a 2 volt peak-to-peak signal across the coil and 1 volt from the source. With this value of resistor and a 10 volt supply the current taken was just 15µA, so this circuit may find applications in "micropower" designs. With a dual-ganged variable capacitor for C1 and C2 it could form a useful basis for an RF signal generator.

*Components for Figure 5.9a*

*Resistor* (all metal film, 0.6W)
R1              4k7

*Capacitor*
C1, 2           select for frequency required (2 off)

*Coil*
L1              select for frequency required

*Semiconductor*
TR1             2N3819 N-channel FET

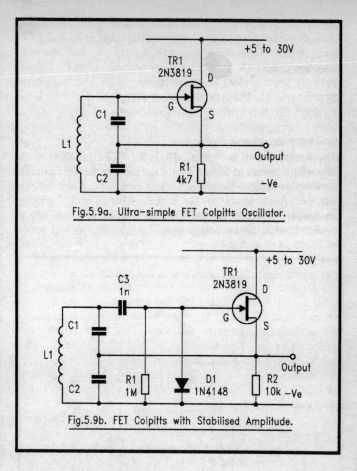

Fig.5.9a. Ultra—simple FET Colpitts Oscillator.

Fig.5.9b. FET Colpitts with Stabilised Amplitude.

*Components for Figure 5.9b*

*Resistors* (all metal film, 0.6W)
R1          1M
R2          10k

*Capacitors*
C1, 2       select for frequency required (2 off)
C3          1n polyester or polystyrene

101

**Two-FET Oscillator**

This circuit, shown in Figure 5.10, is the FET equivalent of the 2-transistor circuit of Figure 5.4a. Like most of the FET circuits it is simpler because the biasing is less complicated and the output waveform tends to be better. Also like its bipolar counterpart it needs no taps for the feedback since this is provided, with the necessary gain, through the second active

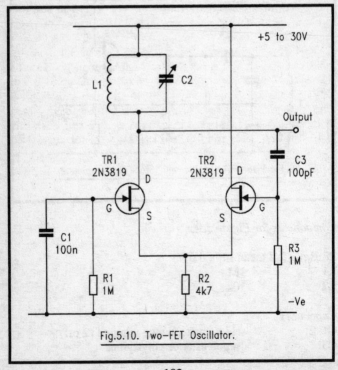

Fig.5.10. Two—FET Oscillator.

device. The high input impedance of the gate of FET TR2 allows the use of a small value for feedback capacitor C3, which reduces the load on the resonant circuit L1 and C2.

The amplitude of oscillation in this circuit can be controlled by varying the value of the common source resistor R2. A high voltage output can be achieved; with the component values shown, at a frequency of about 1MHz and with a supply of 10 volts a signal of 40 volts peak-to-peak was measured across the coil L1 whilst the current drawn from the supply was just half a milliamp. Increasing the value of R2 reduces the signal amplitude and with 100k it dropped to around 4 volts peak-to-peak. However, with low supply voltages and a high value of R2 the circuit may sometimes fail to start up when power is applied. In general, values of R2 between 4k7 and 22k should ensure correct operation. With inefficient (low "Q") resonant circuits, values of less than 4k7 may be needed. The values of L1 and C2 will depend on the frequency required, the circuit was tried with a wide assortment of coils and capacitors, all of which worked well.

The increased complexity of this circuit makes it less suitable than some of the others for high frequency operation. However, trials showed that it should be reliable up to at least 10MHz. Like the bipolar version, it should also be possible to add modulation by replacing R2 with a modulated current source, though the more variable characteristics of FETs would probably entail the use of a preset adjustment for the level of this.

*Components for Figure 5.10*

*Resistors* (all metal film, 0.6W)
R1, 3            1M (2 off)
R2               4k7

*Capacitors*
C1               100n polyester
C2               see text
C3               100p polystyrene

*Coil*
L1               see text

TR1, 2        2N3819 N-channel FET (2 off)

## CMOS LC Oscillators

CMOS inverting gates can be used instead of transistors and
FETs as amplifiers in the construction of oscillator circuits. Any
of the usual configurations can be built with them, though in
practice the simplest and most practical is probably the Colpitts
circuit. Figure 5.11 shows the basic arrangement, which often
will be all that is needed. The two capacitors each have one end
connected to ground and it can be seen that this is actually the
capacitor "tap". The usual formula can be used for
calculating the frequency that will be produced, remembering

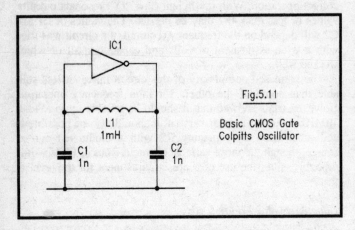

Fig.5.11

Basic CMOS Gate
Colpitts Oscillator

IC1

L1
1mH

C1
1n

C2
1n

that the effective capacitance is the value of both of them in
series. Often they will be equal in value, so the total will be half
of either of them. The example shown was tested with a 1mH
choke for L1 and two 1n polystyrene capacitors for C1 and C2,
which gave about 225kHz. With a 100µH choke and the same
capacitors, it ran at just over 700kHz. The gate used was one of
the four in a 4011B quad NAND gate with the two inputs
connected together, though any of the CMOS inverters should
work.

Apart from using just one gate, a CMOS LC oscillator built

in this way gives much more predictable results than CR types at high frequencies, as the frequency depends almost entirely on the resonant components and is affected little, if at all, by factors such as the propagation delay of the device. Typically it will operate up to the maximum speed the gate is capable of, remembering that this depends to some degree upon the supply voltage. The waveform at the gate input is usually fairly pure, but at the drive end, across C2, it may show some distortion due to loading by the output of the gate. This can be improved if necessary by placing a resistor between the gate output and the junction of L1/C2. The value required will depend on the coil and capacitor in use, but something between 1k and 10k will generally be suitable.

Since other gates can be used, it follows that one of the two provided for oscillator construction in a 4060B divider will work in this arrangement. Figure 5.12 shows this with a 100µH choke and a pair of fixed capacitors C1 and C3, plus the preset trimmer C2 for fine adjustment. With the values shown the frequency will be around 1.638MHz and the trimmer will permit accurate adjustment so that the output from pin 1, the divide-by-4096 output, is exactly 400Hz. When set to this with a supply of 10 volts, this circuit deviated by less than ±4Hz over a supply voltage range of 5 to 15 volts, a variation of less than 0.5%. This gives some idea of the stability that can be expected. With a 220µH choke for L1 and the same capacitors, the output from pin 15 (divide-by-1024) can be adjusted to 1000Hz. With different values for L and C, this oscillator also ran happily at 5MHz with supplies as low as 5 volts, which was considerably faster than the stated performance for this IC. Should the primary oscillator frequency be needed for use elsewhere in a circuit, the best place to obtain it is from the output of the second internal oscillator gate, which appears at pin 9.

*Components for Figure 5.12*

*Capacitors*

| | |
|---|---|
| C1 | 150pF polystyrene |
| C2 | 5–65pF preset trimmer |
| C3 | 220pF |

*Coil*
L1
choke

100μH or 220μH miniature wire-ended
(see text)

*Semiconductor*
IC1

4060B CMOS 14-stage divider with internal
oscillator.

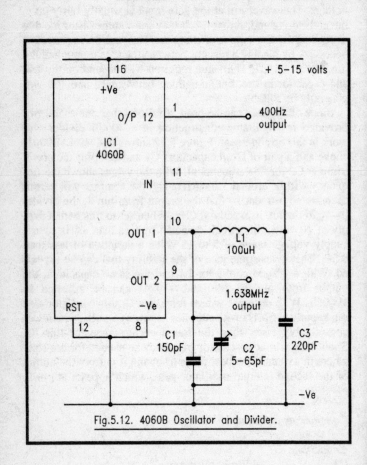

Fig.5.12. 4060B Oscillator and Divider.

## Two-gate CMOS LC Oscillator

It is possible to do away with the need for a tapped capacitor in the CMOS LC oscillator circuit by using two gates. A simple circuit for this is shown in Figure 5.13a. The resonant frequency of this is set by a single untapped coil and capacitor, which will be useful in some designs.

The output of the first gate G1 drives the input of the second G2 so that the overall phase shift of the pair is zero and feedback from the output to the input is positive. Meanwhile local negative DC feedback from the output of G1 to its input through R1 ensures that this gate operates in the active, linear state. The resonant circuit is driven through the resistor R2 and the positive feedback is taken from it through capacitor C1. This is an extremely reliable circuit that will nearly always work well even with very inefficient, low-Q coils. The author has used this in the past to drive metal detector "search coils", air-cored coils with odd shapes and diameters of 15cm or more, using three gates of a 4011B in parallel for G2 to increase power. Apart from the simplicity, the rail-to-rail resistive nature of the CMOS outputs ensured good amplitude stability, and detectors using the circuit usually gave excellent performance.

With the component values shown the circuit will oscillate at about 160kHz, though other values of L1 and C2 can be used to change this. It operates well at very low frequencies. Most of the metal detector designs operated at about 15kHz, though one experimental design used just 2.5kHz as the search frequency! The value of R2 will depend on the efficiency of the resonant circuit, but should be chosen so that the waveform across this is a fairly pure sinewave with a peak-to-peak value close to the supply voltage, which will ensure clean switching of the gates. Too much drive will cause distortion and may affect frequency stability.

*Components for Figure 5.13a*

*Resistors* (all metal film, 0.6W)
R1          1M
R2          1k

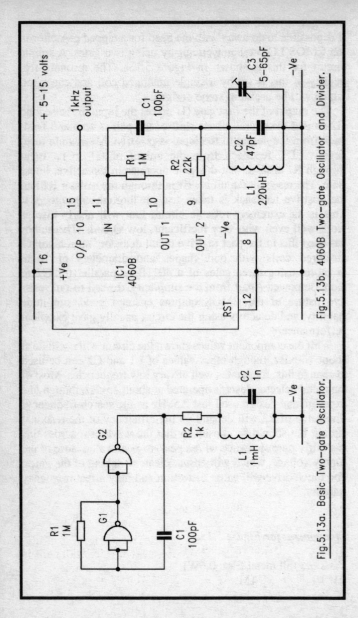

**+ 5–15 volts**

**1kHz output**

C1 100pF

R1 1M

R2 22k

L1 220uH

C2 47pF

C3 5–65pF

**−Ve**

IC1 4060B

16 +Ve

15 O/P 10

11 IN

10

9

OUT 1

OUT 2

8 −Ve

12 RST

Fig.5.13b. 4060B Two-gate Oscillator and Divider.

G1

G2

R1 1M

C1 100pF

R2 1k

L1 1mH

C2 1n

**−Ve**

Fig.5.13a. Basic Two-gate Oscillator.

*Capacitors*
C1                100pF polystyrene
C2                1n polystyrene

*Coil*
L1                1mH (see text)

*Semiconductors*
G1, G2            4011B CMOS quad NAND gate (any invert-
                  ing gates can be used in this circuit) (2 off)

This circuit can also be implemented with the oscillator gates of the 4060B IC, as shown in Figure 5.13b. The component values shown here give an output from pin 15 that can be adjusted to precisely 1000Hz. An efficient ferrite-cored miniature inductor was used for L1 when trying this, which led to the high value used for R2. The stability was found to be not quite as good as the Colpitts version of Figure 5.12, but was still much better than a CR type. It is fairly simple to design this circuit so that it has a reasonably wide range of adjustment.

*Components for Figure 5.13b*

*Resistors* (all metal film, 0.6W)
R1                1M
R2                22k

*Capacitors*
C1                100pF polystyrene
C2                47pF polystyrene
C3                5–65pF trimmer

*Coil*
L1                220µH (see text)

*Semiconductors*
IC1               4060B CMOS 14-stage divider with built-in
                  oscillator.

# Chapter 6

## CRYSTAL OSCILLATOR CIRCUITS

### Crystal Oscillator

For truly precise and stable frequency generation there is no substitute for a crystal-controlled oscillator. At one time crystals were expensive and difficult for the amateur to obtain, but nowadays many are cheap and readily available from normal component suppliers. Crystals do not readily lend themselves to the design of tuneable oscillators, as they can only be pulled a fraction of a percent from their nominal frequencies, but this very fact makes them ideal for the accurate generation of spot frequencies. Often the required frequency will be available "off the shelf", and where it isn't it can often be generated with the help of a divider IC.

A problem for the amateur is that often the full information regarding the crystal to be used is not available. Since crystal characteristics vary quite widely, this can make the design of oscillators using discrete amplifying devices such as FETs and bipolar transistors a bit of a hit and miss process. For this reason these will be avoided in this book, and the most basic designs shown will be those using inverting gates in CMOS devices to provide the necessary gain. Some fully integrated "power up and go" oscillator ICs will be described, as these are the simplest and most reliable method of generating an accurate frequency. These have built-in programmable dividers, allowing several frequencies to be obtained from the one IC with clean, buffered squarewave outputs.

One further device that will be described is the Harris HA7210, a fairly recent introduction to the market. This is a sort of "halfway house", in that it uses an external crystal but can be easily programmed to the optimum internal circuit configuration for various frequencies, and it has a number of other features for low power consumption and reliable, stable operation.

### Single-gate Crystal Oscillator

This is one of the cheapest ways to construct a crystal

oscillator, using a single inverting logic gate. As mentioned in the introduction it may not always work due to the variable characteristics of crystals, but it is more likely to operate correctly than its discrete transistor and FET equivalents. It can be especially useful with 32.768kHz "watch crystals". Some optimisation of component values is usually needed, so an oscilloscope should be available to check operation and waveforms.

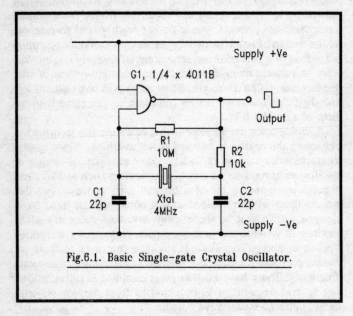

Fig.6.1. Basic Single-gate Crystal Oscillator.

The version of the circuit shown in Figure 6.1, uses one of the four NAND gates in a CMOS 4011B. It is similar to the LC Colpitts circuit in that the capacitors C1 and C2 provide a "tap" to give a 180 degree phase shift from amplifier output to input, which adds to the inversion provided by the gate to give the positive feedback necessary so that oscillation can take place. Resistor R2 is chosen to adjust the drive to the crystal to a reasonable level and with C2 it also forms a low-pass filter to encourage oscillation to take place at the correct frequency instead of a higher "overtone" frequency, as can sometimes occur. The high value resistor R1 provides DC negative feedback to bias the gate into an active amplifying condition and maintain this.

The values of capacitors C1, C2 and resistor R2 will generally need adjustment to suit the characteristics of the particular crystal in use. With a pair of 22pF polystyrene capacitors and a 10k resistor for R2 the prototype circuit worked well with a 4MHz crystal from the author's "junk box", but two different types of 100kHz crystal required 100pF and 2200pF respectively for C2. Increasing the value of the capacitors will lower the frequency slightly, and a variable "trimmer" is often used for fine tuning adjustment, though it should be appreciated that the degree of variation that can be obtained in this way is very small, usually less than 0.1%.

Inspection of the waveforms at the output of the gate and the two ends of the crystal will usually reveal any problems. The gate output will normally be a squarewave, although due to the output impedance of a CMOS device there may be some distortion caused by the load. Parasitic oscillation, indicated by multiple glitches at the crossing points, may indicate a need for higher values of C2, R2, or perhaps both. The input side of the crystal, driven through R2, may have anything from a distorted squarewave through a triangle wave to something approaching a sinewave. The important point is that it should not have a large content of frequencies higher than that intended. The output side, to C1 and the gate input, will usually have a cleaner sinewave although this may be difficult to check as this part of the circuit has a high impedance and can be adversely affected by loading from the test equipment used. A "×10" probe, perhaps with a small DC blocking capacitor, may help here.

This circuit usually works well with "watch crystals". These are sometimes referred to as "tuning fork" crystals because of the shape to which they are cut to achieve low frequency in a very small size, although this cannot be seen as they are always totally enclosed in metal cans. Their frequency is 32.768kHz which, when divided by 2 to the power of 15, results in a 1Hz signal for timekeeping applications. A problem with these crystals is that they are intended for use with circuits powered from just 1.5 volts, so driving them from outputs supplied with much higher voltages can result in failure. They need very little drive anyway, so the value of R2 should be raised to 100k. In tests, a couple of crystals obtained from a major component supplier withstood a supply of 15 volts, but others taken from defunct watches and clocks have failed even with 5 volts. For reliability the best course is probably to purchase the crystal from a regular supplier and restrict the supply to 5 volts. Otherwise, it may be worth operating from just 3 volts, as the circuit will still operate from this with a "micropower" supply current. C1 and C2 should normally be somewhere between 10pF and 22pF, and making one of them, usually C2, adjustable allows accurate frequency adjustment for timekeeping applications.

Any of the usual inverting gates can be used with this circuit. Where a 2-input gate is used, one of these can be tied to an appropriate supply rail as shown to reduce loading on the crystal. Other gates in the same IC could be used for output buffering or gating. Crystal oscillators are usually rather slow to start up due to the very high "Q" of the crystal, so where the signal is to be started and stopped rapidly it is better to keep the actual oscillator running and gate the signal elsewhere.

This is a general purpose circuit that may be useful in some simple applications, but for a circuit needing a divider, or total reliability, some of the following solutions may be better.

### A 4060B Crystal Oscillator
One of the gates of the internal oscillator inside a 4060B can be used to construct a crystal oscillator, and the IC will then provide a number of frequencies from the outputs of the internal binary divider. As only one of the two oscillator gates is required a buffered output with oscillator frequency can be taken from the other, which may be useful when testing or setting up the circuit. Figure 6.2 shows the circuit, using pin 10 as the output to drive the crystal through 100k resistor R2, and pin 11 as an input for the feedback. DC negative feedback to maintain the gate in its active region is applied through R1, and the buffered output of oscillator frequency is available from pin 9. The "reset" pin 12 should be permanently tied to negative supply.

Most of the comments relating to the previous single-gate oscillator apply to this circuit. As it is specifically intended for

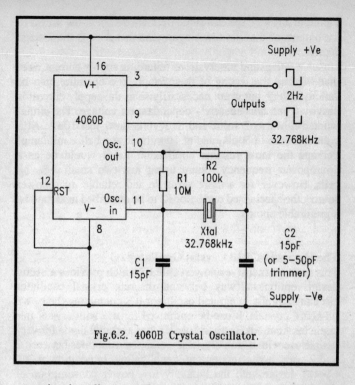

Fig.6.2. 4060B Crystal Oscillator.

operation in a linear mode as an oscillator, the gate between pins 10 and 11 is less prone to spurious oscillation and glitches than most single CMOS gates. It will work with a variety of crystals, but the value of R2 and the two capacitors will need to be chosen to suit these. A frequency of 4MHz was readily achieved using 10k for R2 and two 22pF capacitors. A watch crystal can be used as before, using a 100k resistor for R2 and fine tuning it by varying the value of C1 or C2, usually C2 which can be a 5–50p trimmer. Any of the available divider outputs can be used, but with a 32.768kHz crystal the final output, from pin 3, gives the oscillator divided by 2 to the power of 14, which is 2Hz. Sadly, it is impossible to obtain a 1Hz signal without using another IC for the single extra divider stage, but where this is done some extra circuitry can be added for generating any other frequencies needed such as 30-second or

1-minute pulses. Note that some dividers do not allow access to the outputs of the first few stages. One that does is the 7-stage 4024B.

Some interesting observations regarding supply current were made during the testing of this circuit. The operation can be "micropower", but is not necessarily so as the supply current is heavily – and non-linearly – dependant on voltage. The circuit worked down to 2 volts, and at 3 volts drew just 10µA. At 5 volts this rose to 50µA, and at 10 volts it was half a milliamp! Perhaps the most suitable application for it would be as a micropower frequency source using just two small 1.5 volt cells. However, for a more versatile and reliable micropower source, the specialised oscillator IC to be described next may be a preferable choice.

## The Harris HA7210 Crystal Oscillator IC

This is an inexpensive and versatile IC which provides a useful design option halfway between discrete crystal oscillator circuits and fully integrated oscillator ICs containing their own on-board crystals. It can be optimised for use with crystal frequencies from 10kHz up to 10MHz, has a special mode for very simple use with watch crystals, works from supplies between 2 and 7 volts, and offers output signal gating. In addition, it is a CMOS device with the typically low power consumption of this family; in fact with a watch crystal and a low voltage supply it will operate with a drain of less than 10µA, allowing literally years of operation from a couple of small 1.5 volt cells.

The connections for the 8-pin DIL version of the IC are shown in Figure 6.3, which is also the simplest circuit configuration for a low-frequency crystal. The supply is connected to pin 1 (positive) and pin 4 (negative). The recommended supply voltage is from 2 to 7 volts with an absolute maximum of 10 volts. This allows the use of unregulated batteries with between 2 and five 1.5 volt cells, whilst a regulated 5 volt supply is ideal. Direct connection to a 9 volt battery is inadvisable, but where a PP3 is to supply the circuit a cheap and simple solution is the inclusion of four silicon diodes, such as 1N4148's, in series with the positive supply to pin 1. The total voltage drop across these will reduce the supply to a safe value without incurring

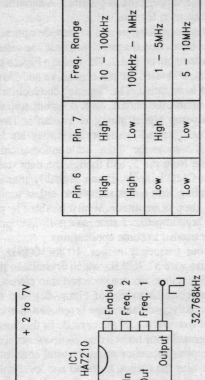

| Pin 6 | Pin 7 | Freq. Range |
|-------|-------|-------------|
| High | High | 10 – 100kHz |
| High | Low | 100kHz – 1MHz |
| Low | High | 1 – 5MHz |
| Low | Low | 5 – 10MHz |

Frequency Range Selection

Fig.6.3. HA7210 Pin Functions.

the additional current that would be taken by a regulator and it's cheaper too! Note the provision of capacitor C1. The manufacturers recommend that a 100n decoupling capacitor is always provided, as close to the supply pins as possible. A ceramic or polyester type should be used for this.

The HA7210 has four operating modes to provide optimum conditions for crystals of various frequencies. These are selected by connections made to pins 6 and 7. The table in Figure 6.3 shows these, where "high" means the pin is positive and "low" means it is connected to negative. The "enable" connection to pin 8 can be used to inhibit the output. As it does not stop the oscillator, instant start-stop signal gating is available. These three pins have internal "pull-up" resistors so if they are left unconnected they will assume the "high" state automatically. The output is available from pin 5, and though the data states that it can drive two CMOS inputs, it can probably manage more than this as loading with a 10k resistor to either supply rail causes only a tiny drop in amplitude. Whilst disabled by pin 8 the output goes to a high impedance state, so a pull-up or pull-down resistor may be needed in some applications.

The first of the four frequency ranges, 10 to 100kHz, is intended mainly for use with 32.768kHz watch crystals. In this mode two internal 15pF capacitors are switched into circuit to provide an arrangement similar to that of Figure 6.1, and the internal power supply to the oscillator stage is reduced to about three volts to prevent overdriving of the crystal. In this mode the device can be operated with no external components apart from the supply decoupling capacitor and the crystal connected across pins 2 and 3, whilst the output, buffered and level-shifted into a rail-to-rail squarewave, is available at pin 5. For operation in this mode no connections are necessary to pins 6, 7, or 8. Whilst this may be accurate enough for some applications, where the circuit forms part of a clock or timing system frequency trimming may be needed for precise adjustment. This can be done with the addition of two fixed capacitors and a trimmer as shown in Figure 6.4, which will allow accurate setting with most watch crystals. Note the unusual connection of the two fixed capacitors to the positive supply rail rather than the negative; this is recommended by the manufacturer. Once set up, the circuit is remarkably stable as the IC compensates

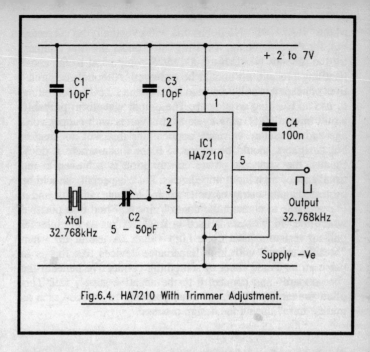

Fig.6.4. HA7210 With Trimmer Adjustment.

for supply voltage and temperature variations and automatically adjusts the crystal drive amplitude to a suitable level.

For other frequencies the appropriate range can be selected with pins 6 and 7 and the crystal simply connected across pins 2 and 3. Where the crystal frequency is on the borderline between two modes, for example 1MHz, both could be tried. The makers suggest that the higher frequency mode may often be preferable in such cases. Usually the oscillator will operate without problems, even with the odd selections of old crystals often found in experimenters' junk boxes. It probably offers the simplest and most reliable way to construct an oscillator for use with an external crystal.

A few precautions should be observed when using the HA7210 device. The first concerns its name! The DIL package of the one used in testing these circuits bears the marking "HA7210IP". The "I" in the suffix can be mistaken for a "1", and in fact has led a leading supplier to list it in their catalogue as the "HA72101". No doubt this will eventually be corrected but, for the time being, if it isn't listed under the first number, try the second! Next, this is a CMOS component so the usual handling precautions should be observed. Although it is relatively cheap, it is still painful to lose around £2.00 by forgetting to use an earthing wrist strap. The output waveform probably won't have a 50:50 duty cycle as this varies with supply voltage and frequency. In many applications this will not matter, but designers should be aware of it for those where it does. Finally, the very low power consumption is achieved at the usual cost of high input impedances. Pin 2 especially should be protected against stray capacitance and leakage currents, and it is preferable to connect the control pins 6, 7 and 8 to positive where the "high" state is used in final designs as the internal pull-up resistors have quite high values. A useful tip when "breadboarding" with high impedance devices like this is to place an insulated sheet of something conductive beneath the "breadboard" and connect it to the negative supply rail. This often prevents problems of stray coupling to sources such as mains "hum" during the design process.

## Single Chip Crystal Oscillators

For simplicity and ease of use it is hard to beat a ready-made crystal oscillator "module". These have been around for some time. Originally they were expensive, fairly large, produced only one frequency and were thirsty in terms of supply current. Some still are, but there are now some that are not. The EXO-3 series of ICs are especially recommended to designers as an inexpensive source of accurate frequencies.

The EXO-3 IC contains a complete oscillator circuit, including the crystal, within a single 8-pin DIL package. Also within the IC is a programmable divider stage that can be set to divide the fundamental frequency by a powers of two from one to eight, so that nine different frequencies are obtainable from the single IC. Although not a "micropower" device, it uses CMOS technology so the supply current is small enough to allow use in battery-operated circuits. There are four versions of the device, differing only in primary oscillator crystal frequency, so for most applications there will be a frequency that is close

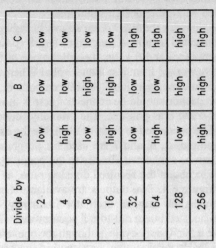

| Divide by | A | B | C |
|---|---|---|---|
| 2 | low | low | low |
| 4 | high | low | low |
| 8 | low | high | low |
| 16 | high | high | low |
| 32 | low | low | high |
| 64 | high | low | high |
| 128 | low | high | high |
| 256 | high | high | high |

Divider Programming

Fig.6.5. EXO-3 Pin Functions.

enough to the one required. The cost of one of these chips is typically around £3.00, so they will often prove cost-effective in comparison with other design solutions.

The connections for the EXO-3 are shown in Figure 6.5. The supply is connected to pins 4 (negative) and 8 (positive) and should be between 3 and 6 volts, though the one tested by the author actually worked from less than 2 volts! Where available, a regulated 5 volt supply is ideal. A 100n ceramic or polyester decoupling capacitor should be connected across the supply as close to pins 4 and 8 as possible. The "standby" control input, pin 3, should be connected to positive to enable the oscillator to run. The three pins 5, 6, and 7 are used for programming the divider and can be connected directly to the positive and negative supplies to obtain the required division ratio, as shown in the table in figure 6.5. Two outputs are available. One is from pin 1, supplying the original oscillator frequency, internally buffered and boosted into a rail-to-tail squarewave. This output may not have a 50:50 duty cycle, although the one tested by the author, the 12MHz version, was very good in this respect. The next output, from pin 2, is also buffered and, since it is the product of at least one stage of division, it always has a precise 50:50 duty cycle. With light loads both these outputs swing practically from rail to rail. They can drive heavier loads than the Harris IC described earlier, a 1k load causes only a very slight loss of output amplitude.

The frequency is not trimmable, but being crystal-controlled is very accurate. A check on the output of the one tested showed a deviation from the set frequency of 0.000125%, which in a timing context is equal to just over 3 seconds a month. This is not to say that all EXO-3's will be this good, but it does suggest they are accurate enough for most purposes.

Whilst the maximum supply current is stated to be 20mA this varies with the crystal frequency, so this is the "worst case" for the highest frequency version which has an oscillator running at nearly 20MHz, and most examples probably won't draw anything like this. The 12MHz one tested drew just 2.6mA from a 5 volt supply and 1.1mA at 3 volts, making it very economical for such a high frequency.

The "standby" input connection, pin 3, is normally connected to positive supply to "enable" the oscillator action.

Connecting it to negative stops the oscillator and consequently reduces the device supply current to a few microamps. In this state both outputs go to the "low" or negative state, and can still sink current from loads connected to them. The "start-up" time when pin 3 goes high is stated to be a maximum of 1.5ms, which is rapid for a crystal oscillator, so in many applications gating the signal with this input will be a useful option.

The four primary oscillator frequencies available are 12MHz, 14.31818MHz, 16MHz, and 19.6608MHz. Readers can check the outputs available from the dividers of these for themselves, using a calculator to divide by two up to eight times. However, it will be seen that the 16MHz version will give a precise 1MHz output when the divider is set to divide by 16. There is no reason why extra stages of division cannot be added using any of the CMOS dividers, and when checked with a calculator it will be found that a few extra stages applied to the 19.6608MHz device will produce all the commonly used data baud rate frequencies between 75Hz and 19.2kHz. A couple of 4024B 7-stage dividers could generate them all simultaneously.

The EXO-3 device was chosen for this section because it is very inexpensive and simple to use, although other fully integrated crystal oscillator ICs are available. Two that might be of interest are the PXO 600 and PXO 1000, both supplied in 16-pin DIL form. These are similar to the EXO-3 but have six divider programming pins and are each capable of generating fifty-seven different output frequencies. The PXO 600 spans a range from one cycle every 200 seconds to 600kHz, and the PXO 1000 covers approximately two minutes per cycle to 1MHz. These ICs are also visually interesting since they have quartz windows through which their crystals can be seen! Unfortunately they are slightly more expensive at around £15.00, though this is still relatively cheap for such a device. A data sheet covering both versions is available to designers wishing to use one of them.

# Chapter 7

# PRACTICAL CONSTRUCTION METHODS

**Audio Oscillator Construction**

Following all the theoretical information, it seemed a good idea to end with a chapter on construction techniques using a practical example for readers to try out for themselves. Most of the circuits described can be constructed on 0.1″ stripboard, which allows testing and experiments to be carried out with ease.

Stripboard is often used for prototype work because it permits immediate construction without the effort of designing and etching a printed circuit board, or the cost and delay of ordering and waiting for delivery should one be available ready-made. Results can be almost as neat and reliable as a PCB so many one-off designs never progress beyond stripboard construction. Many enthusiasts keep a permanent stock of the board ready for use whenever the need arises.

There are some disadvantages with stripboard construction. With its breaks and links, and the care needed to ensure that components are correctly placed, it takes longer to construct than a printed circuit. The links, particularly on a board containing mostly logic ICs, can take up quite a lot of space as well as construction time. The paths taken by the circuit are often rather tortuous so, if a fault occurs, it can be troublesome to locate. This is compounded by the relative ease with which solder "bridges" can accidentally occur across tracks and tiny strips of copper can escape removal around the edges of "breaks". Compared with glassfibre PCB the material is rather fragile, so care is sometimes needed in handling and securing it. It is not suitable for 240 volt mains use, so any parts of the circuit using this or a similar high voltage will have to be constructed separately, and it is not always appreciated that there is quite a high capacitance between adjacent tracks, usually several picofarads, which may cause problems in high frequency circuits.

Some precautions need to be taken to avoid these potential problems, and the nature of the circuit to be built will have some bearing on these. Straightforward analogue circuits, where the signal follows a single linear path through the circuit, will normally cause no problems. More complex circuits may be easier to work with if constructed as a series of modules, or at least as separate areas on the board so that if a fault is present, it will be simpler to locate. Digital circuits with multiple signal paths are perhaps better not constructed on stripboard. They have a nasty habit of developing into "link farms" and can be very difficult indeed to trouble-shoot.

For all but the simplest circuits, it is advisable to draw up a layout on paper before commencing construction. A sheet of paper with a pattern of dots spaced at about 0.15″ is very useful for drafting layouts, one of these can be made with a pen and then photocopied for future use. A fine-tipped (0.5mm) pencil and a pencil-style eraser then make drafting relatively easy. The sections of track actually forming the circuit can be indicated on this, making later trouble-shooting or modification easier. When drafting the layout, sensitive areas of track, those with high impedance, low signal levels or high frequencies, should be kept as short as possible to minimise the effects of leakage and stray capacitance. A useful trick with a very sensitive track is to connect those on each side of it to ground to form a simple "guard ring".

Finally, during construction, it is often a good idea to construct the circuit a bit at a time if possible, testing each part as work progresses. The use of DIL sockets for ICs assists with this and allows the easy recovery of expensive components if the board is scrapped at some later time.

The Wien Bridge oscillator from Chapter 3 has been chosen as an example of layout and construction as it can be built as a relatively compact unit and will provide a useful test instrument for many constructors. The board should first be cut to size. Although 16 strips of 44 holes are shown, constructors may wish to make it longer or wider to simplify fixing to a case or chassis. The underside with the breaks is shown in Figure 7.2. Although breaks can be made by twiddling a twist drill between the fingers, a small inexpensive tool is available for the job and is well worth purchasing if regular use of stripboard is envisaged. As mentioned above, tiny strips of copper sometimes remain around the edges of breaks and can be difficult to see with the naked eye, so a check with a powerful magnifying

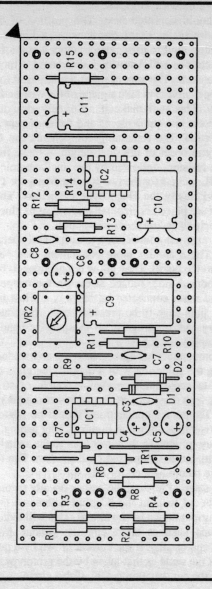

Fig.7.1. The Component Layout for the Wien Bridge Oscillator.

glass is advisable before continuing.

The links should be fitted next. The position of these is shown with those of the other components in Figure 7.1. If appearance matters, and to many constructors it does, the links can make or break the job! Anyway, a neat board is more likely to be a reliable one. The way to make a really neat link with bare tinned copper wire is to take a piece of the wire and stretch it very slightly. This will make it absolutely straight, after which it can be cut into short pieces and the ends bent at right angles for insertion. The remaining components can then be fitted, generally in order of physical height to make life easy. This means the resistors, followed by the small ceramic capacitors and the DIL sockets for the two ICs, the transistor TR1, the preset VR2 and finally the electrolytic capacitors. The three largest of these are placed horizontally so a spot of glue before insertion will help to secure them in position.

To simplify external connections to stripboard special pins are available. These are far more convenient than soldering wires directly to the board. They allow connections to be made from the component side, reduce stress on the copper strips themselves, and wires connected in this way are less likely to break off. The pins have to be pressed very firmly into place before soldering and, once again, an inexpensive hand tool is available to simplify the job.

Once the components have been inserted and soldered, it's worth checking the soldering with a magnifying glass because it's far easier to accidentally bridge a couple of stripboard tracks than it is with those of a PCB, and it's also harder to spot such bridges. Temporary connections should be made to the external components as shown in Figure 7.3 for testing, though it isn't necessary to wire all the capacitors to the switch, a single pair of them can be connected on their own. The two 15n components are recommended for this.

As the first stage of testing, the author usually recommends powering the board without the ICs, but with some means of checking the current drawn by the circuit. This will indicate any drastic problems such as short circuits without destroying expensive ICs and usually, if the current drawn by a published circuit is about the same as that taken by the prototype, there is a good chance the construction is OK. If this circuit is supplied

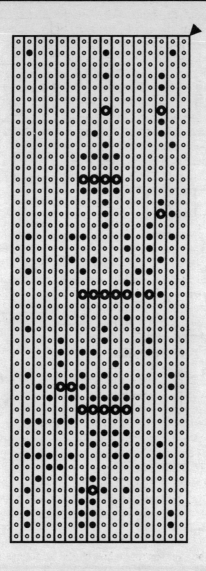

Fig.7.2. The Underside of the Wien Bridge Board.

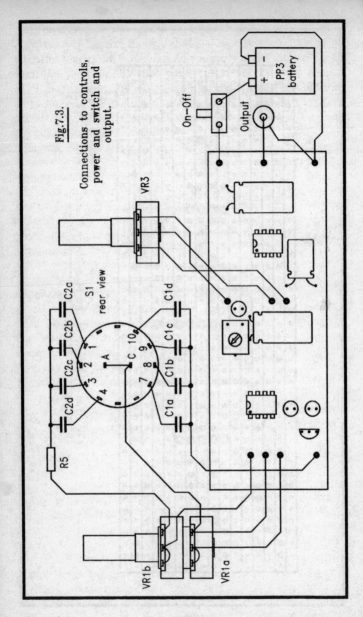

Fig. 7.3.
Connections to controls, power and switch and output.

130

with 9 volts, following a surge as the electrolytic capacitors charge, the current taken should be about 1.5mA. The next step is to fit IC1 and power the circuit again. This should raise the supply current to about 9mA, and with VR1 at about half-travel it should be possible to measure the AC output from IC1a (pin 1) with a meter and set it to around 350mV RMS. If the circuit is OK the DC level measured at pins 1 and 7 of IC1 should both be at about half the supply voltage. If an oscilloscope is available, this can be used instead of a meter for checking and setting up the circuit.

Once the oscillator is working IC2 can be fitted and connections made to the level control VR3, which will raise the supply current to about 10.6mA. It's unlikely there will be any problems with this simple part of the circuit, so the final task is simply to set the maximum output level to 1 volt RMS, using the preset VR2 for this adjustment with VR3 set to maximum.

The project is completed by wiring the capacitors to the switch S1 as shown in Figure 7.3, using the four unused tags on the switch as supports if necessary, and connecting this and the other controls to the board. Ribbon cable can be used to give a neat final appearance. None of the connections should need screening providing they are kept fairly short. A good method of construction is to secure everything to a metal panel which can then be "grounded" to the negative supply. This will minimise the effects of stray capacitance. As described in chapter 3, the power supply can be anything from 6 to 30 volts, so a 9 volt battery can be used, or a simple mains supply, perhaps with a 78LO12 regulator to minimise hum.

*Components for Figure 7.1*

As given for Figures 3.4 and 3.5, plus:
2 × 8-pin DIL sockets
Case, knobs, socket, on-off switch, battery connector.

## Squarewave Output for the Wien Bridge Project

An oscillator circuits of this type is often provided with a squarewave output in addition to the sinewave. Rich in harmonics, this can be used for a variety of tests, or it might be employed to synchronise another piece of equipment such as an oscilloscope to the test signal, often necessary when using the main signal at small amplitudes. "Squaring" of the signal is usually done by applying gain to the main signal until the amplifying device output is driven into saturation in both directions.

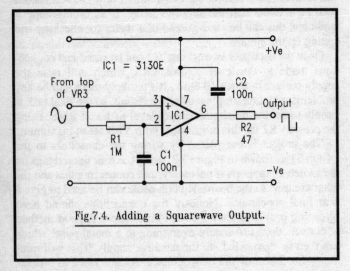

Fig.7.4. Adding a Squarewave Output.

The 3130E op-amp is particularly suitable for this as its output can swing all the way to both supply rails and its "slew rate", the speed with which its output voltage can change, is faster than many other types. Figure 7.4 shows a circuit using one of these devices. The input signal is taken from the top of the amplitude control VR3. It is connected directly to the non-inverting input of IC1, and through the low-pass filter R1 and C1 to the inverting input. The filter ensures that only the average DC voltage of the input is applied to this input, not the signal itself. IC1 acts as a comparator, so when the direct input is above the average level its output is high, when it is below it the output is low. No frequency compensation is used with the op-amp in this circuit. Since it is not expected to behave in a linear fashion compensation is unnecessary and in fact would only slow down the output. The resistor R2 protects the output and ensures stability with capacitive loads. The local decoupling capacitor C2 is advisable to prevent spikes being introduced into the power supply.

This simple circuit provides a squarewave output with a good waveform all the way up to 100kHz and is more than adequate for use with the Wien Bridge project. It can be constructed as an add-on for the main board, or perhaps built on a small extension of it.

One small precaution that should be observed with this circuit is to keep the supply below 15 volts, as this is the maximum permitted for the 3130E device.

*Components for Figure 7.4*

*Resistors* (all metal film, 0.6W)
R1          1M
R2          47

*Capacitors*
C1, 2       100n ceramic (2 off)

*Semiconductors*
IC1         3130E CMOS op-amp.

*Notes*